Legal Information

MW00629021

Thank You!

Thank you so much for choosing this book!

Discover 66 awesome projects that you can easily print using a 3D printer (preferably FDM). The best thing is, that all files of the featured objects can be downloaded for free! This book not only offers inspiration but also gives valuable tips on slicing and actual printing. The projects are subdivided into categories and levels of difficulty. You will find very easy, but useful, up to very complex and fascinating objects in this book. Start now, get inspired and materialize many great objects!

If you are just getting started with 3D printing also take a look at the corresponding book: "3D printing 101 - The Ultimate Beginners Guide". It´ll show you exactly how to achieve high-quality results in 3D printing. If you would like to realize your own ideas and learn how to design objects, take a look at the corresponding book: "CAD 101 - The Ultimate Beginners Guide". Both books are available at amazon.com.

Table of Contents

Legal Information 1

Thank You! 1

Table of Contents... 2

1 How to Use this Book 5

2 General: Useful & Practical 7

2.1 Key Holder 7

2.2 Money Clip (double version) 10

2.3 Money Clip (single version) 12

2.4 (Shopping-) Bag Holder 14

2.5 Smartphone Stand (foldable) 16

2.6 Cable Holder 18

2.7 Foldable Knife 20

2.8 Minimal Wallet 23

2.9 Webcam Cover.. 26

2.10 Bookmark... 28

2.11 Nail Brush.. 30

2.12 Emergency Whistle 32

2.13 Pages Holder 34

2.14 Doorstop (Snowflake) 36

2.15 Cart Token (Euro) 38

2.16 Door bolt (printed fully functionable) 40

2.17 Headphone Stand 42

2.18 Snap Hook... 45

3 Household: Kitchen 47

3.1 Coffee Grinder 47

3.2 Bag Clip 50

3.3 Coffee Tamper 52

3.4 Heart Pattern (Coffee) 54

3.5 Snowflake Pattern (Coffee) 56

3.6. Cookie-Cutter: Cupcake 58

3.7 Cookie-Cutter: Lion (3D) 60

3.8 Cookie-Cutter: Triceratops Dinosaur (3D) 62

3.9 Curved Wine Stand 64

3.10 Nutcracker 66

3.11 Drip Mat.. 69

3.12 Bottle Opener 71

3.13 PET-Bottle Opener 73

3.14 Can Handle.. 75

4 Household: Bathroom **77**

4.1 Comb 77

4.2 Tube Squezzer..79

5 Art & Decoration.. **81**

5.1 2D-Wall Art: Elephant 81

5.2 2D-Wall Art: Tree 83

5.3 Big Dice 85

5.4 Sculpture: Hug me Ghost 87

5.5 Sculpture: Saber-toothed Cat Skull 90

5.6 Decoration: Rose.. 94

5.7 Sculpture: T-Rex Skull... 96

5.8 Sculpture: Human Skull.. 100

5.9 Sculpture: Low-Poly-Dog.. 103

5.10 Sculpture: Low-Poly-Horse.. 105

5.11 Honeycomb-Vase.. 107

6 Toys & Games **109**

6.1 "4 in a row".. 109

6.2 Air-Spinner... 112

6.3 Puzzle: Animals 114

6.4 Gordian Knot.. 116

6.5 Board Game: Wobbly Chess.................................... 118

6.6 Toy: Airplane 123

7 Storage **127**

7.1 SD-Card Storage 127

7.2 Towel Hook 129

7.3 Bag Hooks 131

7.4 Bowl.. 134

8 Tool-Accessories **136**

8.1 Driller Dust Container 136

8.2 Pliers Stand 139

8.3 Machine Vise.. 142

8.4 Platform Jack (printed fully assembled) 146

9 Complex Objects (fully functional) **148**

9.1 Mechanical Clock 148

9.2 Luxo Jr. Lamp (Pixar) 153

10 Fun & Other **157**

10.1 Cryptex.. 157

10.2 Bee Hotel 161

10.3 Butterfly (articulated) 163

10.4 Present Ornament (lockable) 165

10.5 Micro Catapult 169

10.6 Keyring: Heart 171

10.7 Bearing (printed fully functionable) 173

11 Closing Remarks **175**

Appendix: Slicing Settings (Cura & CR-10) **176**

1 How to Use this Book

Gather a lot of inspiration for 3D printing by reading this book. On the following pages you will find a selection of 3D printing projects for the realization with a Fused Deposition Modeling (FDM) 3D printer. Each project includes a photo and a short description of the object and valuable tips on slicing settings, positioning and how to carry out the entire 3D printing process. The presented projects can be downloaded online (for free) as ".stl" files. The respective links are given.

The slicing software used in this book is Cura by Ultimaker. You can download this program for free at the website www.ultimaker.com (-> Products -> Ultimaker Cura). Most slicing programs offer very similar features. So you can use your favorite software like Slic3r, Simplify3D or others as well. An optimized settings-profile for slicing can be downloaded free of charge from www.3ddruckworkshop.de/startpaket. Additionally, all general slicing settings can be found in the appendix of this book. All slicing settings that have to be individually changed for the respective project are also listed, so that 3D printing becomes as easy as never before!

A CR-10 from Creality is used as a 3D printer. The CR-10 uses the FDM method. The CR-10 series is highly recommended due to its excellent printing quality and easy operation. If you want to buy a 3D printer, take a look at the newer versions such as the CR-10S, CR10-X or CR-10S Pro. Further descriptions of these devices can be found at https://de.creality3d.cn. PLA(+) from Sunlu (or 3DHero) or Tianse is used and recommended as filament. Of course you can also use the 3D printer you may already own. If you don't have your own 3D printer, or if you don't want to buy one, I recommend to search for a makerspace or to use 3D printing service providers (online).

A makerspace is a place where usually several and different devices, such as 3D printers, laser scanners or laser cutters, can be accessed freely by members. These rooms, which have been set up as workshops, offer the necessary space and the right equipment for the realization of your own projects.

Furthermore you can inform yourself online at www.3dhubs.com, whether a (private) 3D printer owner accepts 3D printing orders nearby you. Besides the FDM method, SLS and SLA are often offered, too.

Alternatively you could start with service providers like Protolabs (www.protoblabs.com), Shapeways (www.shapeways.com) and co..

Enough words for the beginning. Let's start with the actual projects! They are divided into different categories and levels of difficulty to make reading and especially searching for amazing projects in this book as easy as possible. For each project, a profile with data such as download link, printing time, difficulty level, etc., is given.

indicates the most difficult level. The addition "+" serves as an additional increase of the respective degree of difficulty (only if necessary).

You will find projects from the following categories on the next pages:

- General: Useful & Practical
- Household: Kitchen
- Household: Bathroom
- Art & Decoration
- Toys & Games
- Storage
- Tool-Accessories
- Complex Objects (fully functional)
- Fun & Other

2 General: Useful & Practical

2.1 Key Holder

2.1.1 Overview:

Difficulty*: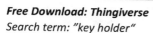
Printing time: 10 h
Material: 81 g

Free Download: Thingiverse
Search term: "key holder"
Designer: "Ronniebravo10"
Downloadlink: https://www.thingiverse.com/thing:3286136
Additionally required: Key rings

* (of 🗿 🗿 🗿 🗿 🗿)

2.1.2 Tips on editing and file positioning:

Rotation of all single objects as in the general view in *fig. 1*:

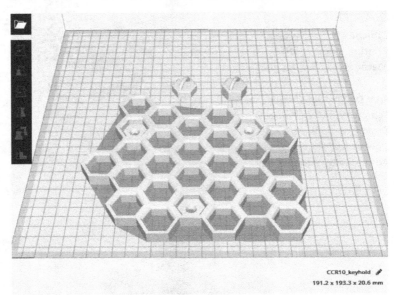

CCR10_keyhold
191.2 x 193.3 x 20.6 mm

Figure 1: General view of all files to be printed

2.1.3 Recommended combination of printing jobs:

1) "Keyholder_version1" *(e.g. black)*
2) "Keyhold (=key)" *(e.g. green)*
3) "short (=key short)" *(e.g. gold)*

2.1.4 Tips on slicing settings for each printing job:

"Keyholder version1":
(Printing time: approx. 7 h)

- Layer height: 0.2 mm
- Infill Percentage: 20%
- Ironing enabled: yes
- Support structure: no

- Bed Adhesion: Skirt (2 lines, 5 mm offset)

"keyhold (=key)":
(Printing time: approx. 2 h (5 pieces)) | downscale by 1 % if too large

- **Quantitiy: e.g. 5 pieces (dependent on the number of keys)**
- Layer height: 0.12 mm
- Infill percentage: 20%
- Ironing enabled: yes
- Support structure: no
- Bed adhesion: Skirt (2 lines, 5 mm offset)

"short (=key short)":
(Printing time: approx. 1 h) | downscale by 1 % if too large

- **Quantitiy: e.g. 3 pieces (for covering the drilling holes)**
- Layer height: 0.12 mm
- Infill percentage: 20%
- Ironing enabled: yes
- Support structure: no
- Bed adhesion: Skirt (2 lines, 5 mm offset)

2.1.5 Positioning on the printing bed (per print job):

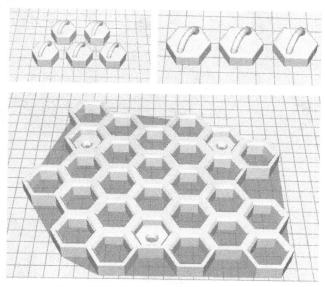

Figure 2: Printing jobs (1 image = 1 printing job)

2.2 Money Clip (double version)

2.2.1 Overview:

Difficulty*:
Printing time: 2 h
Material: 14 g

Free Download: Thingiverse
Search term: "double money clip"
Designer: "kenversus"
Downloadlink: https://www.thingiverse.com/thing:2832388
Additionally required: Money ;)

* (of 🖨 🖨 🖨 🖨)

2.2.2 Tips on editing and file positioning:

e.g. "3D_Printed_Double_Money_Clip" as in *fig. 3:*

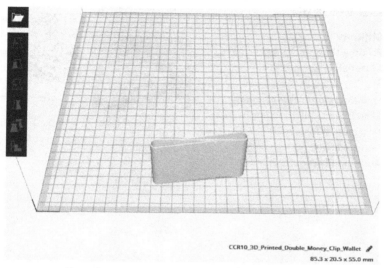

CCR10_3D_Printed_Double_Money_Clip_Wallet
85.3 x 20.5 x 55.0 mm

Figure 3: General view of all files to be printed (1x each)

2.2.3 Tips on slicing settings for each printing job:

"3D_Printed_Double_Money_Clip":
(Printing time: approx. 2 h)

- **Color: e.g. black or gold**
- Layer height: 0.12 mm
- Infill percentage: 100%
- Ironing enabled: yes
- Support structure: no
- Bed adhesion: Brim (width: 6 mm; lines: 15; inside: no)

11

2.3 Money Clip (single version)

2.3.1 Overview:

Difficulty*:
Printing time: **2,5 h**
Material: **7 g**

Free Download: Thingiverse
Search term: "money clips"
Designer: "Ysoft_be3D"
Downloadlink: https://www.thingiverse.com/thing:1385206/files
Additionally required: Money ;)

* (of 🏆 🏆 🏆 🏆)

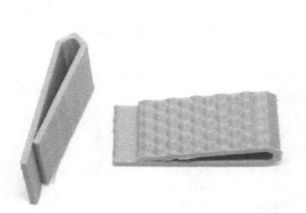

2.3.2 Tips on editing and file positioning:

Two variants as in *fig. 4:*

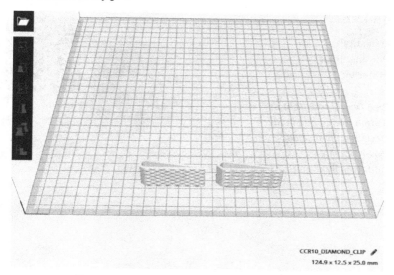

CCR10_DIAMOND_CLIP
124.9 x 12.5 x 25.0 mm

Figure 4: General view of all files to be printed (1x each)

2.3.3 Tips on slicing settings for each printing job:

"3D Printed Double Money Clip":
(Printing time: approx. 2,5 h for printing both variants)

- **Color: e.g. black or gold**
- Layer heigth: 0.12 mm
- Infill percentage: 100%
- Ironing enabled: yes
- Support structure: no
- Bed adhesion: Brim (width: 6 mm; lines: 15; inside: no)

2.4 (Shopping-) Bag Holder

2.4.1 Overview:

Difficulty*:
Printing time: 3 h
Material: 30 g

Free Download: Thingiverse
Search term: "bag holder"
Designer: "ivanseidel"
Downloadlink: https://www.thingiverse.com/thing:26767
Additionally required: ---

* (of)

2.4.2 Tips on editing and file positioning:

Positioning of all single objects as in the general view in *fig. 5:*

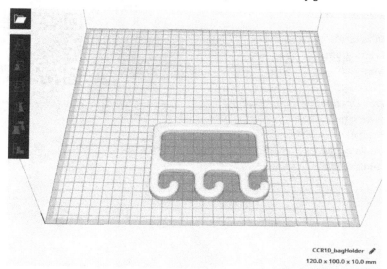

CCR10_bagHolder
120.0 x 100.0 x 10.0 mm

Figure 5: General view of all files to be printed (1x each)

2.4.3 Tips on slicing settings for each printing job:

"bagHolder":
(Printing time: approx. 3 h)

- **Color: e.g. black**
- Layer height: 0.16 mm
- Infill percentage: 50%
- Ironing enabled: yes
- Support structure: no
- Bed adhesion: Skirt (2 lines, 5 mm offset)

2.5 Smartphone Stand (foldable)

2.5.1 Overview:

Difficulty*:

Printing time: **2 h**

Material: **29 g**

Free Download: Thingiverse
Search term: "foldable phone stand"
Designer: "Duals"
Downloadlink: https://www.thingiverse.com/thing:3482186
Additionally required: ---

* (of 🍷 🍷 🍷 🍷)

2.5.2 Tips on editing and file positioning:

Positioning of all single objects as in the general view in *fig. 6:*

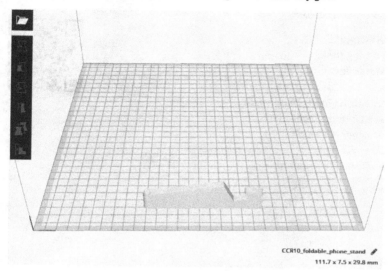

CCR10_foldable_phone_stand

111.7 x 7.5 x 29.8 mm

Figure 6: General view of all files to be printed (1x each)

2.5.3 Tips on slicing settings for each printing job:

"foldable_phone_stand":
(**Printing time: approx. 2 h**)

- **Color: e.g. black**
- Layer height: 0.12 mm
- Infill percentage: 20%
- Ironing enabled: no
- Support structure: no
- Bed adhesion: Skirt (2 lines, 5 mm offset)

Be cautious when opening the folded stand for the first time! If necessary, use a knife or a plier to remove excess filament from the hinge.

2.6 Cable Holder

2.6.1 Overview:

Difficulty*:
Printing time: **40 min**
Material: **5 g**

Free Download: Thingiverse
Search term: "cable holder"
Designer: "bardiaesm"
Downloadlink: https://www.thingiverse.com/thing:70549
Additionally required: ---

* (of)

2.6.2 Tips on editing and file positioning:

Positioning of all single objects as in the general view in *fig. 7:*

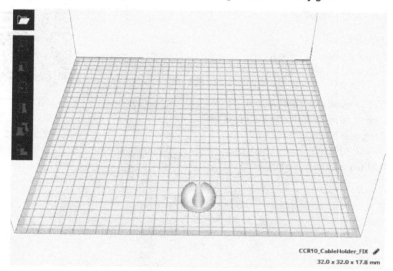

CCR10_CableHolder_FIX
32.0 x 32.0 x 17.8 mm

Figure 7: General view of all files to be printed (1x each)

2.6.3 Tips on slicing settings for each printing job:

"CableHolder_FIX":
(**Printing time: approx. 40 min**)

- **Color: e.g. green or gold**
- Layer height: 0.12 mm
- Infill percentage: 25 %
- Ironing enabled: no
- Support structure: no
- Bed adhesion: Skirt (2 lines, 5 mm offset)

2.7 Foldable Knife

2.7.1 Overview:

Difficulty*:
Printing time: **2.5 h**
Material: **11 g**

Free Download: Thingiverse
Search term: "folding knife letter"
Designer: "DRLex"
Downloadlink: https://www.thingiverse.com/thing:2789193
Additionally required: ---

* (of 🏆 🏆 🏆 🏆)

2.7.2 Tips on editing and file positioning:

Rotation of all single objects as in the general view in *fig. 8*:

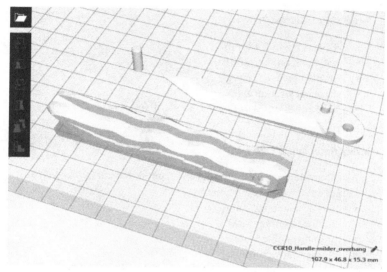

Figure 8: General view of all files to be printed (1x each)

2.7.3 Recommended combination of printing jobs:

1) "Handle-milder_overhang" *(color: e.g. black)*
2) "Blade" (or "Blade-serated")
   (color: e.g. grey)
3) "pin" (additionally maybe "pin-fatter" & "pin-narrower")
   (color: e.g. grey)

2.7.4 Tips on slicing settings for each printing job:

"Handle-milder_overhang":
(**Printing time: approx. 1.5 h**)

- Layer height: 0.12 mm
- Infill percentage: 35%
- Ironing enabled: no
- Support structure: no

21

- Bed adhesion: Skirt (2 lines, 5 mm offset)

"Blade" (or "Blade-serated"):
(Printing time: approx. 20 min)

- Layer height: 0.12 mm
- Infill percentage: 100%
- Ironing enabled: yes
- Support structure: no
- Bed adhesion: Skirt (2 lines, 5 mm offset)

"pin":
(Printing time: approx. 20 min)

- **Quantity: 1x „pin", „pin-fatter", „pin-narrower",** in order to obtain the one which fits best.
- Layer height: 0.12 mm
- Infill percentage: 100%
- Ironing enabled: yes
- Support structure: no
- Bed adhesion: Brim (width: 8 mm; lines: 20; inside: no)

2.7.5 Positioning on the printing bed (per print job):

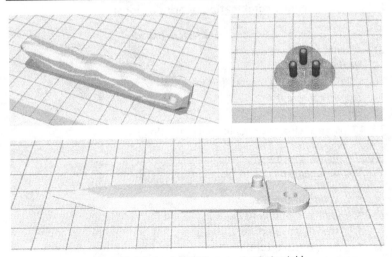

Figure 9: Printing jobs (1 image = 1 printing job)

2.8 Minimal Wallet

2.8.1 Overview:

Difficulty*:	
Printing time:	**6 h**
Material:	**35 g**

Free Download: Thingiverse
Search term: "smart wallet"
Designer: "b03tz"
Downloadlink: https://www.thingiverse.com/thing:3097272
Additionally required: ---

* (of 🏆 🏆 🏆 🏆)

2.8.2 Tips on editing and file positioning:

Rotation of all single objects as in the general view in *fig. 10:*

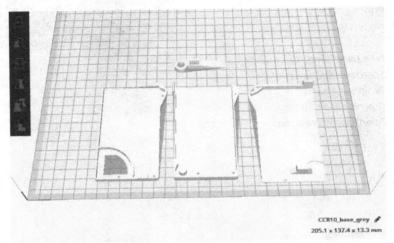

CCR10_base_grey
205.1 x 137.4 x 13.3 mm

Figure 10: General view of all files to be printed (1x each)

2.8.3 Recommended combination of printing jobs:

1) "base_grey" & "lid_grey" *(color: e.g. black)*
2) "lever" & "change_compartment_orange" *(color: e.g. green)*

2.8.4 Tips on slicing settings for each printing job:

"base grey" & "lid grey":
(Printing time: approx. 4 h)

- Layer height: 0.12 mm
- Infill percentage: 25%
- Ironing enabled: yes
- Support structure: no
- Bed adhesion: Skirt (2 lines, 5 mm offset)

24

"lever" & "change compartment orange":
(Printing time: approx. 2 h)

- Layer height: 0.12 mm
- Infill percentage: 25%
- Ironing enabled: yes
- Support structure: no
- Bed adhesion: Skirt (2 lines, 5 mm offset)

2.8.5 Positioning on the printing bed (per print job):

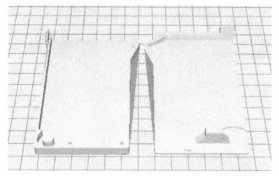

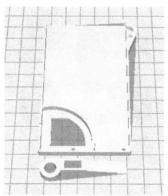

Figure 11: Printing jobs (1 image = 1 printing job)

2.9 Webcam Cover

2.9.1 Overview:

Difficulty*:
Printing time: **10 min**
Material: **1 g**

Free Download: Thingiverse
Search term: "webcam cover"
Designer: "revensanchez"
Downloadlink: https://www.thingiverse.com/thing:3215422
Additionally required: ---

* (of 🏆 🏆 🏆 🏆)

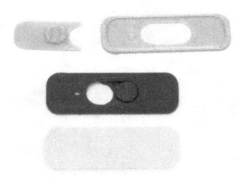

2.9.2 Tips on editing and file positioning:

"webcam_cover" as in fig. *12*

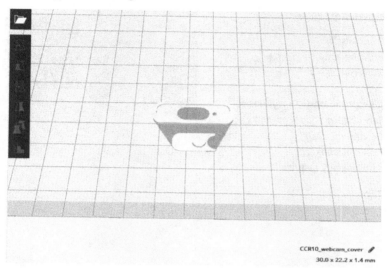

CCR10_webcam_cover ✏
30.0 x 22.2 x 1.4 mm

Figure 12: General view of all files to be printed (1x each)

2.9.3 Tips on slicing settings for each printing job:

"webcam_cover":
(Printing time: approx.. 10 min)

- **Color: e.g. black or gold**
- Layer height: 0.12 mm
- Infill percentage: 100%
- Ironing enabled: yes
- Support structure: no
- Bed adhesion: Skirt (2 lines, 5 mm offset)

2.10 Bookmark

2.10.1 Overview:

Difficulty*:

Printing time: 0.5 h

Material: 3 g

Free Download: Thingiverse
Search term: "bookmark #1"
Designer: "Tosh"
Downloadlink: https://www.thingiverse.com/thing:357481
Additionally required: ---

* (of 🏆 🏆 🏆 🏆)

2.10.2 Tips on editing and file positioning:

"bookmark1" as in fig. *13:*

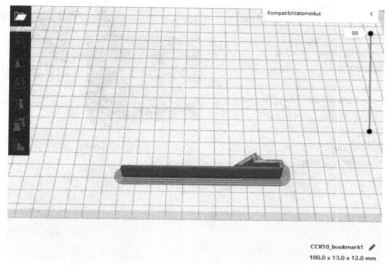

Figure 13: General view of all files to be printed (1x each)

2.10.3 Tips on slicing settings for each printing job:

"bookmark1":

(Printing time: approx. 0.5 h)

- **Color: e.g. blue**
- Layer height: 0.12 mm
- Infill percentage: 100%
- Ironing enabled: yes
- Support structure: no
- Bed adhesion: Brim (width: 6 mm; lines: 10; inside: no)

2.11 Nail Brush

2.11.1 Overview:

Difficulty*:

Printing time: **2 h**

Material: **28 g**

Free Download: Thingiverse
Search term: "nail brush"
Designer: "Turbo_SunShine"
Downloadlink: https://www.thingiverse.com/thing:3355727/files
Additionally required: ---

* (of 🏆 🏆 🏆 🏆)

2.11.2 Tips on editing and file positioning:

Positioning of all single objects as in the general view in *fig. 14*:

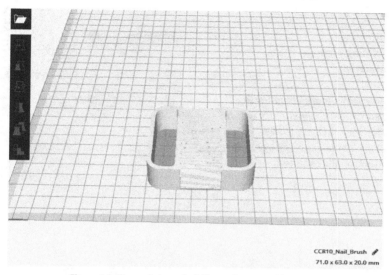

CCR10_Nail_Brush
71.0 x 63.0 x 20.0 mm

Figure 14: General view of all files to be printed (1x each)

2.11.3 Tips on slicing settings for each printing job:

"Nail Brush":
(Printing time: approx. 2 h)

- **Color: e.g. blue**
- Layer height: 0.2 mm
- Infill percentage: 20%
- Ironing enabled: no
- Support structure: no
- Bed adhesion: Skirt (2 lines, 5 mm offset)

2.12 Emergency Whistle

2.12.1 Overview:

Difficulty*:	
Printing time:	**1 h**
Material:	**5 g**

Free Download: Thingiverse
Search term: "emergency whistle"
Designer: "whistleblower"
Downloadlink: https://www.thingiverse.com/thing:2933021
Additionally required: ---

* (of 🏆 🏆 🏆 🏆)

2.12.2 Tips on editing and file positioning:

Rotation of all single objects as in the general view in *fig. 15*:

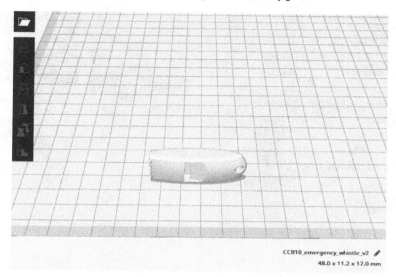

CCR10_emergency_whistle_v2
48.0 x 11.2 x 17.0 mm

Figure 15: General view of all files to be printed (1x each)

2.12.3 Tips on slicing settings for each printing job:

"emergency whistle v2" :
(Printing time: approx. 1 h)

- **Color: e.g. green**
- Layer height: 0.12 mm
- Infill percentage: 100%
- Ironing enabled: yes
- Support structure: no
- Bed adhesion: Skirt (2 lines, 5 mm offset)

2.13 Pages Holder

2.13.1 Overview:

Difficulty*:

Printing time: **45 min**

Material: **5 g**

Free Download: Thingiverse
Search term: "pages holder"
Designer: "Cruele"
Downloadlink: https://www.thingiverse.com/thing:1503676
Additionally required: ---

* (of 🏆 🏆 🏆 🏆)

2.13.2 Tips on editing and file positioning:

Rotation of all single objects as in the general view in *fig. 16:*

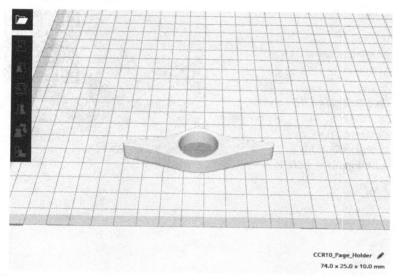

CCR10_Page_Holder
74.0 x 25.0 x 10.0 mm

Figure 16: General view of all files to be printed (1x each)

2.13.3 Tips on slicing settings for each printing job:

"Page Holder":
(Printing time: approx. 45 min)

- **Color: e.g. blue**
- Layer height: 0.12 mm
- Infill percentage: 25%
- Ironing enabled: yes
- Support structure: no
- Bed adhesion: Skirt (2 lines, 5 mm offset)

2.14 Doorstop (Snowflake)

2.14.1 Overview:

Difficulty*:
Printing time: 4.5 h
Material: 45 g

Free Download: Thingiverse
Search term: "snowflake doorstop"
Designer: "fsp"
Downloadlink: https://www.thingiverse.com/thing:2762576
Additionally required: ---

* (of 🏆 🏆 🏆 🏆)

2.14.2 Tips on editing and file positioning:

Rotation of all single objects as in the general view in *fig. 17:*

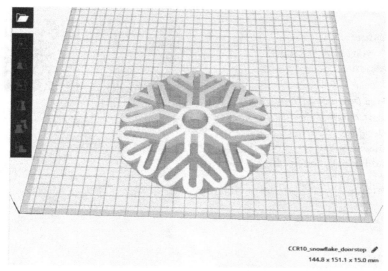

CCR10_snowflake_doorstop
144.8 x 151.1 x 15.0 mm

Figure 17: General view of all files to be printed (1x each)

2.14.3 Tips on slicing settings for each printing job:

"snowflake_doorstop":
(Printing time: approx. 4.5 h)

- **Color: e.g. blue**
- Layer height: 0.2 mm
- Infill percentage: 20%
- Ironing enabled: yes
- Support structure: no
- Bed adhesion: Skirt (2 lines, 5 mm offset)

2.15 Cart Token (Euro)

2.15.1 Overview:

Difficulty*:

Printing time: 0.5 h

Material: 4 g

Free Download: Thingiverse
Search term: "euro cart token"
Designer: "Rubertel"
Downloadlink: https://www.thingiverse.com/thing:2387874
Additionally required: ---

* (of 🏆 🏆 🏆 🏆)

2.15.2 Tips on editing and file positioning:

Rotation of all single objects as in the general view in *fig. 18*:

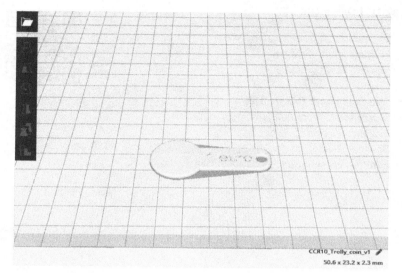

Figure 18: General view of all files to be printed (1x each)

2.15.3 Tips on slicing settings for each printing job:

"Trolly_coin_v1":
(**Printing time: approx. 0.5 h**)

- **Color: e.g. green, red**
- Layer height: 0.12 mm
- Infill percentage: 35%
- Ironing enabled: yes
- Support structure: no
- Bed adhesion: Skirt (2 lines, 5 mm offset)

2.16 Door bolt (printed fully functionable)

2.16.1 Overview:

Difficulty*:
Printing time: 4.5 h
Material: 44 g

Free Download: Thingiverse
Search term: "door bolt"
Designer: "Bogul"
Downloadlink: https://www.thingiverse.com/thing:1596180
Additionally required: ---

* (of 🏆 🏆 🏆 🏆)

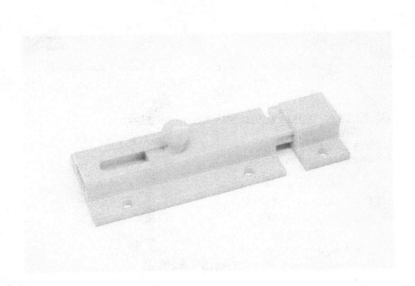

2.16.2 Tips on editing and file positioning:

Rotation of all single objects as in the general view in *fig. 19*:

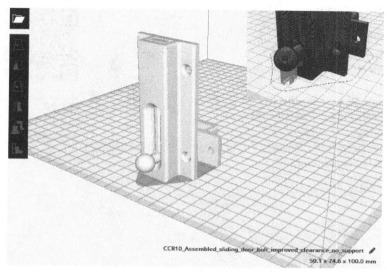

Figure 19: General view of all files to be printed (1x each)

2.16.3 Tips on slicing settings for each printing job:

"Assembled sliding door bolt improved clearance no support":
(**Printing time: approx. 4.5 h**)

- **Color: e.g. green**
- Layer height: 0.2 mm
- Infill percentage: 25%
- Ironing enabled: yes
- **Support structure: yes (Angle: 60°, Percentage: 15 %,** mode: only touch printing bed**) as in *fig. 19***
- Bed adhesion: Skirt (2 lines, 5 mm offset)

41

2.17 Headphone Stand

2.17.1 Overview:

Difficulty*:
Printing time: **8 h**
Material: **47 g**

Free Download: Thingiverse
Search term: "headphone stand"
Designer: "Jeroen_H"
Downloadlink: *https://www.thingiverse.com/thing:2483037*
Additional required: ---

* (of   )

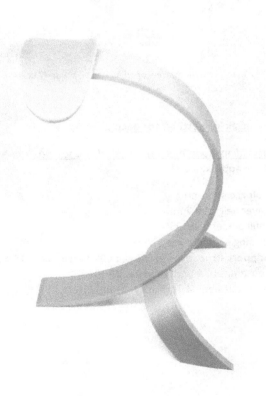

2.17.2 Tips on editing and file positioning:

Rotation of all single objects as in the general view in *fig. 20:*

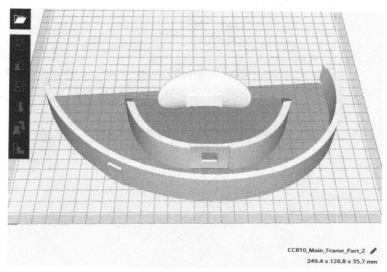

CCR10_Main_Frame_Part_2
249.4 x 126.8 x 35.7 mm

Figure 20: General view of all files to be printed (1x each)

2.17.3 Recommended combination of printing jobs:

1) "Main_Frame_Part_1" & "Main_Frame_Part_2"
   (color: e.g. gold)
2) "Headphone_Rest" *(color: e.g. gold)*

2.17.4 Tips on editing and file positioning:

"Main Frame Part 1" & "Main Frame Part 2":
(**Printing time: approx. 7 h**)

- Layer height: 0.16 mm
- Infill percentage: 25%
- Ironing enabled: yes
- Support structure: no
- Bed adhesion: Skirt (2 lines, 5 mm offset)

"Headphone_Rest":
(Printing time: approx. 1 h)

- Layer height: 0.16 mm
- Infill percentage: 25%
- Ironing enabled: no
- **Support structure: yes (Angle: 60°, Percentage: 15 %) as in *fig. 21***
- Bed adhesion: Brim (width: 8 mm; lines: 20; inside: yes)

2.17.5 Positioning on the printing bed (per print job):

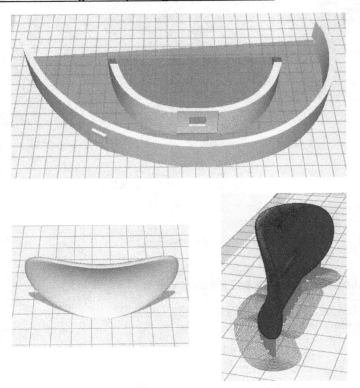

Figure 21: Printing jobs (1 image = 1 printing job)

2.18 Snap Hook

2.18.1 Overview:

Difficulty*:

Printing time: 1 h

Material: 8 g

Free Download: Thingiverse
Search term: "carabiner clip"
Designer: "ZRAFT"
Downloadlink: https://www.thingiverse.com/thing:221727
Additionally required: ---

* (of 🏆 🏆 🏆 🏆)

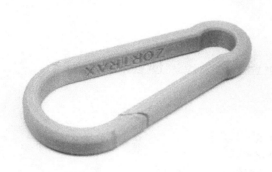

2.18.2 Tips on editing and file positioning:

Rotation of all single objects as in the general view in *fig. 22*:

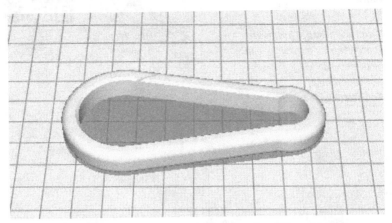

Figure 22: General view of all files to be printed (1x each)

2.18.3 Tips on slicing settings for each printing job:

"zortrax_carabiner":
(Printing time: approx. 1 h)

- **Color: e.g. gold**
- Layer height: 0.12 mm
- Infill percentage: 50%
- Ironing enabled: yes
- Support structure: no
- Bed adhesion: Skirt (2 lines, 5 mm offset)

3 Household: Kitchen

3.1 Coffee Grinder

3.1.1 Overview:

Difficulty*:
Printing time: 15.5 h
Material: 135 g

Free Download: Thingiverse
Search term: "Coffee Grinder"
Designer: "Clarkerubber"
Downloadlink: *https://www.thingiverse.com/thing:2205644/files*
Additionally required: 7 x M3x10 or M3x15 mm bolts

* (of 🍷 🍷 🍷 🍷)

3.1.2 Tips on editing and file positioning:

Rotation of all single objects as in the general view in *fig. 23:*

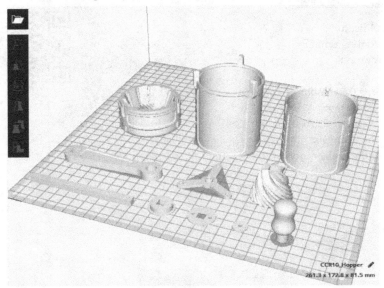

Figure 23: General view of all files to be printed (1x each)

3.1.3 Recommended combination of printing jobs:

1) "Hopper" & "Tray" *(color: e.g. black)*
2) "Axel"; "Arm"; "BearingA"; "BearingB"; "Bracket"; "Knob_Washer" *(color: e.g. black)*
3) "OuterGrinder"; "InternalGrinder"; "Knob" *(color: e.g. green)*

3.1.4 Tips on slicing settings for each printing job:

"Hopper" & "Tray":
(Printing time: approx. 7.5 h)

- Layer height: 0.16 mm
- Infill percentage: 20%
- Ironing enabled: no
- Support structure: no
- Bed adhesion: Skirt (2 lines, 5 mm offset)

_"Axel"; "Arm"; "BearingA"; "BearingB"; "Bracket"; "Knob_Washer":_
(Printing time: approx. 2 h)

- Layer height: 0.12 mm
- Infill percentage: 25%
- Ironing enabled: yes
- Support structure: no
- Bed adhesion: Skirt (2 lines, 5 mm offset)

"OuterGrinder"; "InternalGrinder"; "Knob":
(Printing time: approx. 6 h)

- Layer height: 0.16 mm
- Infill percentage: 55%
- Ironing enabled: no
- Support structure: no
- Bed adhesion: Skirt (2 lines, 5 mm offset)

3.1.5 Positioning on the printing bed (per print job):

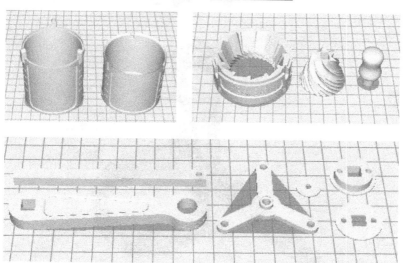

Figure 24: Printing jobs (1 image = 1 printing job)

3.2 Bag Clip

3.2.1 Overview:

Difficulty*:
Printing time: **1 h**
Material: **7 g**

Free Download: Thingiverse
Search term: "bag clip"
Designer: "paulbelcher"
Downloadlink: https://www.thingiverse.com/thing:47053
Additionally required: ---

* (of 🏆 🏆 🏆 🏆)

3.2.2 Tips on editing and file positioning:

Positioning of all single objects as in the general view in fig. *25:*

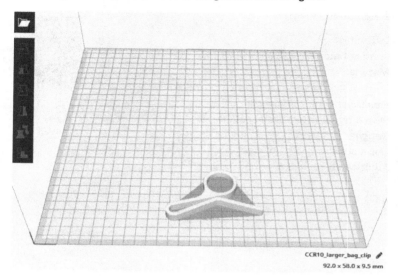

CCR10_larger_bag_clip ✏
92.0 x 58.0 x 9.5 mm

Figure 25: General view of all files to be printed (1x each)

3.2.3 Tips on slicing settings for each printing job:

"larger bag clip":
(Printing time: approx. 1 h)

- **Color: e.g. black**
- Layer height: 0.16 mm
- Infill percentage: 35%
- Ironing enabled: yes
- Support structure: no
- Bed adhesion: Skirt (2 lines, 5 mm offset)

3.3 Coffee Tamper

3.3.1 Overview:

Difficulty*:
Printing time: 3 h
Material: 10 g

Free Download: Thingiverse
Search term: "coffee tamper 52"
Designer: "xR1stos"
Downloadlink: https://www.thingiverse.com/thing:3001218
Additionally required: ---

* (of 🏆 🏆 🏆 🏆)

3.3.2 Tips on editing and file positioning:

Positioning of all single objects as in the general view in fig. *26:*

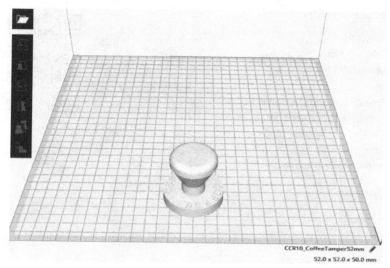

CCR10_CoffeeTamper52mm
52.0 x 52.0 x 50.0 mm

Figure 26: General view of all files to be printed (1x each)

3.3.4 Tips on slicing settings for each printing job:

"CoffeeTamper52mm" or "CoffeeTamper54mm" (depending on machine):
(Printing time: approx. 3 h)

- **Color: e.g. black**
- Layer height: 0.12 mm
- Infill percentage: 30%
- Ironing enabled: yes
- Support structure: no
- Bed adhesion: Skirt (2 lines, 5 mm offset)

3.4 Heart Pattern (Coffee)

3.4.1 Overview:

Difficulty*:
Printing time: **45 min**
Material: **4 g**

Free Download: Thingiverse
Search term: "coffee gauge heart"
Designer: "thomaskoch"
Downloadlink: https://www.thingiverse.com/thing:1753249
Additionally required: ---

* (of 🏆 🏆 🏆 🏆)

3.4.2 Tips on editing and file positioning:

"Coffee_gauge_Heart" as in *fig. 27:*

CCR10_Coffee_gauge_Heart ✏
95.0 x 75.0 x 1.0 mm

Figure 27: General view of all files to be printed (1x each)

3.4.3 Tips on slicing settings for each printing job:

"Coffee_gauge_Heart":
(**Printing time: approx. 45 min**)

- **Color: e.g. white**
- Layer height: 0.16 mm
- Infill percentage: 20%
- Ironing enabled: yes
- Support structure: no
- Bed adhesion: Skirt (2 lines, 5 mm offset)

3.5 Snowflake Pattern (Coffee)

3.5.1 Overview:

Difficulty*:
Printing time: **45 min**
Material: **4 g**

Free Download: Thingiverse
Search term: "snowflake coffee"
Designer: "Lore2106"
Downloadlink: https://www.thingiverse.com/thing:2929856
Additionally required: ---

* (of 🏆 🏆 🏆 🏆)

3.5.2 Tips on editing and file positioning:

"snowflake" as in *fig. 28:*

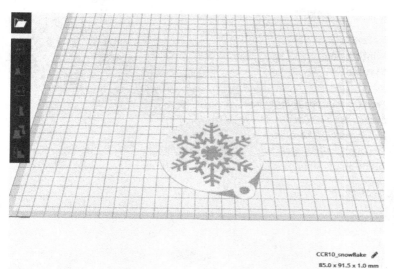

CCR10_snowflake
85.0 x 91.5 x 1.0 mm

Figure 28: General view of all files to be printed (1x each)

3.5.3 Tips on slicing settings for each printing job:

"snowflake":
(Printing time: approx. 45 min)

- **Color: e.g. white**
- Layer height: 0.16 mm
- Infill percentage: 20%
- Ironing enabled: yes
- Support structure: no
- Bed adhesion: Skirt (2 lines, 5 mm offset)

3.6. Cookie-Cutter: Cupcake

<u>**3.6.1 Overview:**</u>

Difficulty*:
Printing time: **2 h**
Material: **15 g**

Free Download: Thingiverse
Search term: "cupcake cookie"
Designer: "ErickArmenta"
Downloadlink: <u>https://www.thingiverse.com/thing:2892744</u>
Additionally required: ---

* (of 💺 💺 💺 💺)

3.6.2 Tips on editing and file positioning:

"Cortador_Cupcake_10cm" as in *fig. 29:*

CCR10_Cortador_Cupcake_10cm ✐
87.7 x 108.8 x 14.0 mm

Figure 29: General view of all files to be printed (1x each)

3.6.3 Tips on slicing settings for each printing job:

"Cortador_Cupcake_10cm":
(Printing time: approx. 2 h)

- **Color: e.g. white**
- Layer height: 0.2 mm
- Infill percentage: 20%
- Ironing enabled: no
- Support structure: no
- Bed adhesion: Skirt (2 lines, 5 mm offset)

3.7 Cookie-Cutter: Lion (3D)

3.7.1 Overview:

Difficulty*:
Printing time: **2.5 h**
Material: **14 g**

Free Download: Thingiverse
Search term: "cookie cutter lion"
Designer: "animus"
Downloadlink: https://www.thingiverse.com/thing:1064238
Additionally required: ---

* (von 🏆🏆🏆🏆)

3.7.2 Tips on editing and file positioning:

1x "mane", 1x "body" und 2x "legs" in a single printing job as in *fig. 30:*

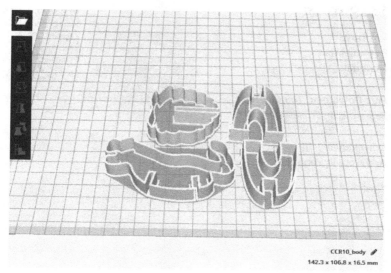

CCR10_body
142.3 x 106.8 x 16.5 mm

Figure 30: General view of all files to be printed (1x each)

3.7.3 Tips on editing and file positioning:

"mane" & "body" & "legs":
(Printing time: approx. 2.5 h)

- **Color: e.g. white**
- Layer height: 0.2 mm
- Infill percentage: 20%
- Ironing enabled: no
- Support structure: no
- Bed adhesion: Skirt (2 lines, 5 mm offset)

3.8 Cookie-Cutter: Triceratops Dinosaur (3D)

3.8.1 Overview:

Difficulty*:
Printing time: **3 h**
Material: **16 g**

Free Download: Thingiverse
Search term: "triceratops cutter"
Designer: "Isolt"
Downloadlink: https://www.thingiverse.com/thing:859431
Additionally required: ---

* (of 🏆 🏆 🏆 🏆)

3.8.2 Tips on editing and file positioning:

1x "Triceratops_Cutter" as in *fig. 31:*

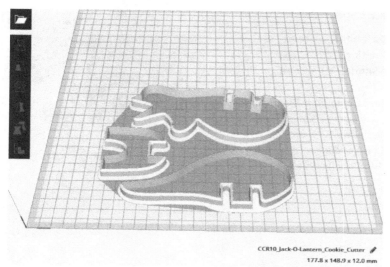

CCR10_Jack-O-Lantern_Cookie_Cutter
177.8 x 148.9 x 12.0 mm

Figure 31: General view of all files to be printed (1x each)

3.8.3 Tips on slicing settings for each printing job:

"Triceratops Cutter":
(Printing time: approx. 3 h)

- **Color: e.g. white**
- Layer height: 0.2 mm
- Infill percentage: 20%
- Ironing enabled: no
- Support structure: no
- Bed adhesion: Skirt (2 lines, 5 mm offset)

3.9 Curved Wine Stand

3.9.1 Overview:

Difficulty*:

Printing time: 6.5 h

Material: 78 g

Free Download: Thingiverse
Search term: "curved wine holder "
Designer: "Chevron42 "
Downloadlink: *https://www.thingiverse.com/thing:1562117/files*
Additionally required: ---

* (of 🍷 🍷 🍷 🍷)

3.9.2 Tips on editing and file positioning:

Positioning of all single objects as in the general view in *fig. 32:*

Figure 32: General view of all files to be printed (1x each)

3.9.3 Tips on slicing settings for each printing job:

"Curved Wine Holder w cutout":
(**Printing time: approx. 6.5 h)**

- **Color: e.g. gold**
- Layer height: 0.2 mm
- Infill percentage: 20%
- Ironing enabled: yes
- **Support structure: yes (Angle: 60°, Percentage: 15 %) as in *fig. 33***
- Bed adhesion: Brim (width: 6 mm; lines: 10; inside: no)

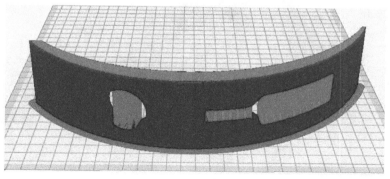

Figure 33: Support structure in blue (Layer view)

3.10 Nutcracker

3.10.1 Overview:

Difficulty*:
Printing time: 6 h
Material: 70 g

Free Download: Thingiverse
Search term: "working nutcracker"
Designer: "RenatoT"
Downloadlink: https://www.thingiverse.com/thing:600723
Additionally required: ---

* (of 🖨 🖨 🖨 🖨)

3.10.2 Tips on editing and file positioning:

Rotation of all single objects as in the general view in *fig. 34:*

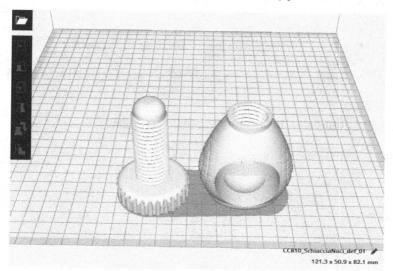

Figure 34: General view of all files to be printed (1x each)

3.10.3 Recommended combination of printing jobs:

1) "Part1_Ok" *(color: e.g. blue)*
2) "Part2_Ok" *(color: e.g. blue)*

3.10.4 Tips on slicing settings for each printing job:

"Part1_Ok" :
(Printing time: approx. 2.5 h)

- Layer height: 0.2 mm
- Infill percentage: 35%
- Ironing enabled: yes
- Support structure: no
- Bed adhesion: Skirt (2 lines, 5 mm offset)

"Part2_Ok":
(Printing time: approx. 3.5 h)

- Layer height: 0.2 mm
- Infill percentage: 35%
- Ironing enabled: yes
- **Support structure: yes (Angle: 60°, Percentage: 15 %) as in** *fig. 35*
- Bed adhesion: Skirt (2 lines, 5 mm offset)

3.10.5 Positioning on the printing bed (per printing job):

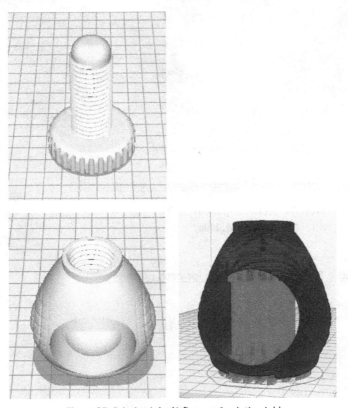

Figure 35: Printing jobs (1 figure = 1 printing job)

3.11 Drip Mat

3.11.1 Overview:

Difficulty*:
Printing time: **5 h**
Material: **43 g**

Free Download: Thingiverse
Search term: "office drip mat"
Designer: "Hunted_One"
Downloadlink: https://www.thingiverse.com/thing:2218288
Additionally required: ---

* (of 🍷 🍷 🍷 🍷)

3.11.2 Tips on editing and file positioning:

Rotation of all single objects as in the general view in *fig. 36:*

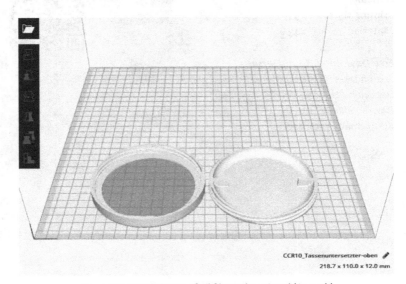

CCR10_Tassenuntersetzter-oben
218.7 x 110.0 x 12.0 mm

Figure 36: General view of all files to be printed (1x each)

3.11.3 Tips on slicing settings for each printing job:

"Tassenuntersetzer-oben" & "Tassenuntersetzer-unten" :
(**Printing time: approx. 5 h**)

- **Color: e.g. green**
- Layer height: 0.16 mm
- Infill percentage: 35%
- Ironing enabled: no
- Support structure: no
- Bed adhesion: Skirt (2 lines, 5 mm offset)

3.12 Bottle Opener

3.12.1 Overview:

Difficulty*:
Printing time: **3 h**
Material: **21 g**

Free Download: Thingiverse
Search term: "bottle opener"
Designer: "Kart5a"
Downloadlink: https://www.thingiverse.com/thing:269463
Additional required: a coin

* (of 🏆 🏆 🏆 🏆)

3.12.2 Tips on editing and file positioning:

Rotation of all single objects as in the general view in *fig. 37:*

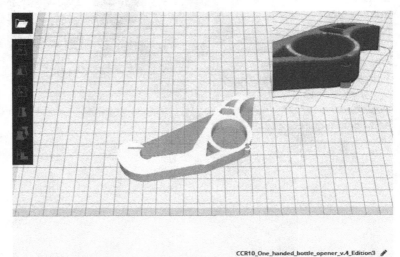

CCR10_One_handed_bottle_opener_v.4_Edition3 ✏
69.1 x 102.9 x 13.6 mm

Figure 37: General view of all files to be printed (1x each)

3.12.3 Tips on slicing settings for each printing job:

"One handed bottle opener v.4 Edition3":
(Printing time: approx. 3 h)

- **Color: e.g. blue**
- Layer height: 0.12 mm
- Infill percentage: 50%
- Ironing enabled: yes
- **Support structure: yes (Angle: 60°, Percentage: 15 %) as in** *fig. 37*
- Bed adhesion: Skirt (2 lines, 5 mm offset)

3.13 PET-Bottle Opener

3.13.1 Overview:

Difficulty*:	
Printing time:	**2 h**
Material:	**9 g**

Free Download: Thingiverse
Search term: "pet opener"
Designer: "EIJIRO"
Downloadlink: https://www.thingiverse.com/thing:3067929/files
Additionally required: ---

* (of 🏆 🏆 🏆 🏆)

3.13.2 Tips on editing and file positioning:

Rotation of all single objects as in the general view in *fig. 38:*

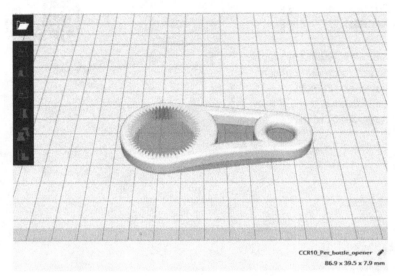

CCR10_Pet_bottle_opener
86.9 x 39.5 x 7.9 mm

Figure 38: General view of all files to be printed (1x each)

3.13.3 Tips on slicing settings for each printing job:

"Pet bottle opener":
(Printing time: approx. 2 h)

- **Color: e.g. red**
- Layer height: 0.12 mm
- Infill percentage: 50%
- Ironing enabled: yes
- Support structure: no
- Bed adhesion: Skirt (2 lines, 5 mm offset)

3.14 Can Handle

3.14.1 Overview:

Difficulty*:

Printing time: **4 h**

Material: **38 g**

Free Download: Thingiverse
Search term: "can handle"
Designer: "ilmandorlone"
Downloadlink: https://www.thingiverse.com/thing:992319
Additionally required: ---

* (of 🏆 🏆 🏆 🏆)

3.14.2 Tips on editing and file positioning:

Rotation of all single objects as in the general view in *fig. 39:*

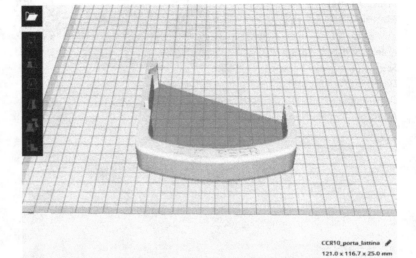

CCR10_porta_lattina
121.0 x 116.7 x 25.0 mm

Figure 39: General view of all files to be printed (1x each)

3.14.3 Tips on slicing settings for each printing job:

"porta lattina":
(Printing time: approx. 4 h)

- **Color: e.g. blue**
- Layer height: 0.16 mm
- Infill percentage: 30%
- Ironing enabled: yes
- Support structure: no
- Bed adhesion: Skirt (2 lines, 5 mm offset)

4 Household: Bathroom

4.1 Comb

4.1.1 Overview:

Difficulty*:
Printing time: **1 h**
Material: **6 g**

Free Download: Thingiverse
Search term: „hair comb"
Designer: „repraprook"
Downloadlink: https://www.thingiverse.com/thing:1140/files
Additionally required: ---

* (of 🏆 🏆 🏆 🏆)

4.1.2 Tips on editing and file positioning:

Positioning of all single objects as in the general view in *fig. 40:*

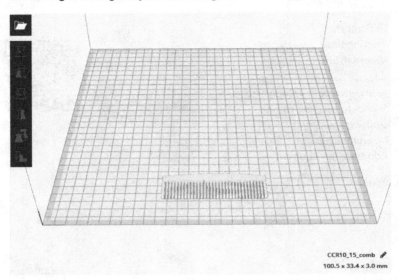

CCR10_15_comb
100.5 x 33.4 x 3.0 mm

Figure 40: General view of all files to be printed (1x each)

4.1.3 Tips on slicing settings for each printing job:

<u>"15_comb":</u>
(Printing time: approx. 1 h)

- **Color: e.g. black**
- Layer height: 0.12 mm
- Infill percentage: 100%
- Ironing enabled: yes
- Support structure: no
- Bed adhesion: Skirt (2 lines, 5 mm offset)

4.2 Tube Squezzer

4.2.1 Overview:

Difficulty*:
Printing time: 3,5 h
Material: 17 g

Free Download: Thingiverse
Search term: "tube squeezer"
Designer: "ottenjr"
Downloadlink: https://www.thingiverse.com/thing:1147252
Additionally required: ---

* (of 🔧🔧🔧🔧)

4.2.2 Tips on editing and file positioning:

Position "20160204_Toothpaste_Roller_print_Rev_C_fixed" as in fig. 41:

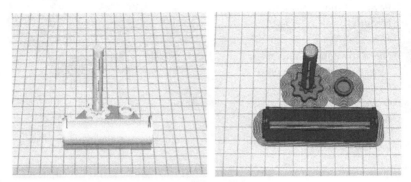

Figure 41: General view of all files to be printed (1x each)

4.2.3 Tips on slicing settings for each printing job:

"20160204_Toothpaste_Roller_print_Rev_C_fixed":
(Printing time: approx. 3.5 h)

- Layer height: 0.12 mm
- Infill percentage: 70%
- Ironing enabled: no
- Support structure: no
- Bed adhesion: Brim (width: 8 mm; lines: 20; inside: no)

5 Art & Decoration

5.1 2D-Wall Art: Elephant

5.1.1 Overview:

Difficulty*:

Printing time:　4.5 h

Material:　30 g

Free Download: Thingiverse
Search term: "low poly elephant"
Designer: "jayzhengwx"
Downloadlink: https://www.thingiverse.com/thing:2710361
Additionally required: ---

* (of 🏆 🏆 🏆 🏆)

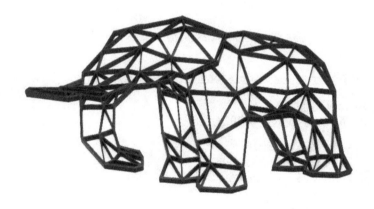

5.1.2 Tips on editing and file positioning:

Positioning of all single objects as in the general view in *fig. 42:*

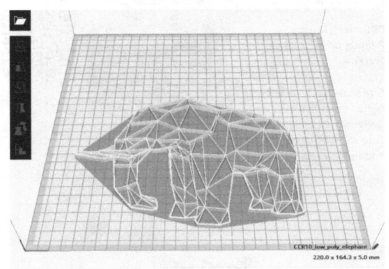

Figure 42: General view of all files to be printed (1x each)

5.1.3 Tips on slicing settings for each printing job:

"low poly elephant":
(**Printing time: approx. 4.5 h**)

- **Color: e.g. black**
- Layer height: 0.16 mm
- Infill percentage: 25%
- Ironing enabled: yes
- Support structure: no
- Bed adhesion: Skirt (2 lines, 5 mm offset)

5.2 2D-Wall Art: Tree

5.2.1 Overview:

Difficulty*:
Printing time: 4.5 h
Material: 40 g

Free Download: Thingiverse
Search term: "Tree 2D Wall art"
Designer: "dtm2477"
Downloadlink: <https://www.thingiverse.com/thing:3164969>
Additionally required: ---

* (of 🏆 🏆 🏆 🏆)

5.2.2 Tips on editing and file positioning:

Positioning of all single objects as in the general view in *fig. 43:*

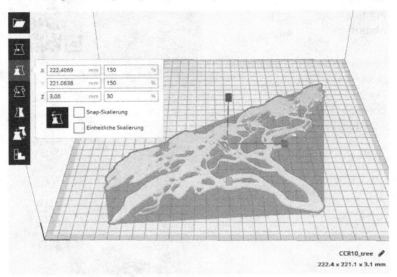

Figure 43: General view of all files to be printed (1x each)

5.2.3 Tips on slicing settings for each printing job:

"tree":
(**Printing time: approx. 4.5 h**)

- **Color: e.g. black**
- Scaling (x: 150% , y: 150%, z: 30%) for faster printing (z) and a larger result (x, y)
- Layer height: 0.16 mm
- Infill percentage: 50%
- Ironing enabled: yes
- Support structure: no
- Bed adhesion: Skirt (2 lines, 5 mm offset)

5.3 Big Dice

5.3.1 Overview:

Difficulty*:
Printing time: **3 h**
Material: **41 g**

Free Download: Thingiverse
Search term: "big dice"
Designer: "Radek476"
Downloadlink: https://www.thingiverse.com/thing:3376965
Additionally required: ---

* (of 🏆 🏆 🏆 🏆)

5.3.2 Tips on editing and file positioning:

"A5--hraci-kostka-6A" as in *fig. 44:*

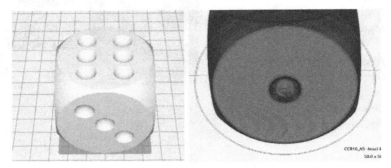

Figure 44: General view of all files to be printed (1x each)

5.3.4 Tips on slicing settings for each printing job:

"A5--hraci-kostka-6A":
(Printing time: approx. 3 h)

- **Color: e.g. black or gold**
- Layer height: 0.12 mm
- Infill percentage: 25%
- Ironing enabled: yes
- **Support structure: yes (Angle: 60°, Percentage: 15 %) as in *fig. 44***
- Bed adhesion: Skirt (2 lines, 5 mm offset)

5.4 Sculpture: Hug me Ghost

5.4.1 Overview:

Difficulty*:
Printing time: 3.5 h
Material: 20 g

Free Download: Thingiverse
Search term: "hug me ghost"
Designer: "GreyBeard3D"
Downloadlink: https://www.thingiverse.com/thing:2604075
Additionally required: ---

* (of 🏆 🏆 🏆 🏆)

5.4.2 Tips on editing and file positioning:

Rotation of all single objects as in the general view in *fig. 45:*

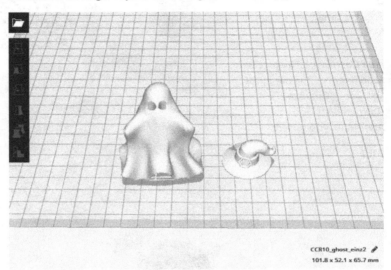

CCR10_ghost_einz2
101.8 x 52.1 x 65.7 mm

Figure 45: General view of all files to be printed (1x each)

5.4.3 Recommended combination of printing jobs:

3) "Ghost_Remix" *(color: e.g. white)*
4) "Witch_Hat_Remix" *(color: e.g. black)*

5.4.4 Tips on slicing settings for each printing job:

"Ghost_Remix":
(**Printing time: approx. 3 h**)

- Layer height: 0.16 mm
- Infill percentage: 25%
- Ironing enabled: no
- **Support structure: yes (Angle: 60°, Percentage: 15 %) as in *fig. 45***
- Bed adhesion: Brim (width: 6 mm; lines: 15; inside: no)

"Witch_Hat_Remix":
(Printing time: approx. 0.5 h)

- Layer height: 0.16 mm
- Infill percentage: 25%
- Ironing enabled: no
- **Support structure: yes (Angle: 60°, Percentage: 15 %) as in *fig. 46***
- Bed adhesion: Skirt (2 lines, 5 mm offset)

5.4.5 Positioning on the printing bed (per print job):

Figure 46: Printing jobs (1 image = 1 printing job)

5.5 Sculpture: Saber-toothed Cat Skull

5.5.1 Overview:

Difficulty*: ♟ ♟ ♟ +
Printing time: 14 h
Material: 87 g

Free Download: Thingiverse
Search term: "saber-toothed cat"
Designer: "MakerBot"
Downloadlink: https://www.thingiverse.com/thing:472463
Additionally required: ---

* (of ♟ ♟ ♟ ♟)

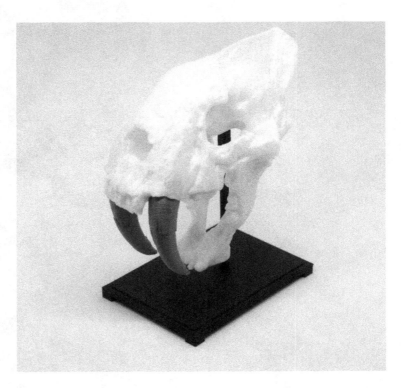

5.5.2 Tips on editing and file positioning:

Rotation of all single objects as in the general view in *fig. 47:*

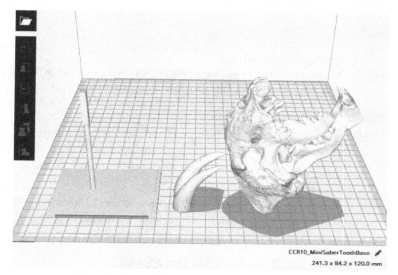

CCR10_MiniSaberToothBase
241.3 x 84.2 x 120.0 mm

Figure 47: General view of all files to be printed (1x each)

5.5.3 Recommended combination of printing jobs:

1) "MiniSaberToothBase" *(color: e.g. black)*
2) "MiniSaberToothSkull" *(color: e.g. white)*
3) "MiniSaberToothSabers" *(color: e.g. grey)*

5.5.4 Tips on slicing settings for each printing job:

"MiniSaberToothBase" :
(Printing time: approx. 2.5 h)

- ▪ Layer height: 0.16 mm
- ▪ Infill percentage: 20%
- ▪ Ironing enabled: yes
- ▪ Support structure: no
- ▪ Bed adhesion: Skirt (2 lines, 5 mm offset)

"MiniSaberToothSkull":
(Printing time: approx. 10.5 h)

- Layer height: 0.16 mm
- Infill percentage: 20%
- Ironing enabled: no
- **Support structure: yes (Angle: 60°, Percentage: 15 %) as in *fig. 48***
- **Bed adhesion: Brim (width: 15 mm; lines: 38; inside: yes)**

"MiniSaberToothSabers":
(Printing time: approx. 1 h)

- Layer height: 0.16 mm
- Infill percentage: 20%
- Ironing enabled: no
- **Support structure: yes (Angle: 60°, Percentage: 15 %) as in *fig. 48***
- **Bed adhesion: Brim (width: 6 mm; lines: 15; inside: no)**

5.5.5 Positioning on the printing bed (per print job):

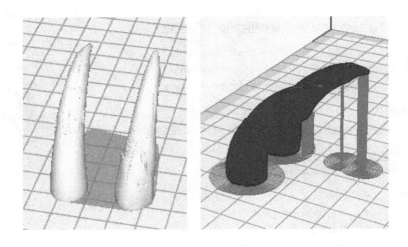

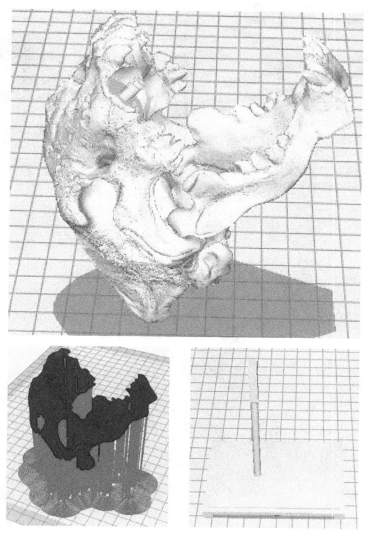

Figure 48: Printing jobs (1 image = 1 printing job)

5.6 Decoration: Rose

5.6.1 Overview:

Difficulty*:

Printing time: **2 h**

Material: **5 g**

Free Download: Thingiverse
Search term: "printable rose"
Designer: "Jerrill"
Downloadlink: https://www.thingiverse.com/thing:283738/files
Additionally required: ---

* (of 🖨 🖨 🖨 🖨)

5.6.2 Tips on editing and file positioning:

Rotation of all single objects as in the general view in *fig. 49:*

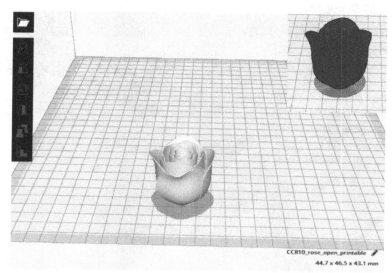

Figure 49: General view of all files to be printed (1x each)

5.6.3 Tips on slicing settings for each printing job:

"rose_open_printable":
(Printing time: approx. 2 h)

- **Color: e.g. red**
- Layer height: 0.12 mm
- Infill percentage: 100%
- Ironing enabled: no
- Support structure: no
- Bed adhesion: Brim (width: 10 mm; lines: 25; inside: yes)

5.7 Sculpture: T-Rex Skull

5.7.1 Overview:

Difficulty*:
Printing time: **21.5 h**
Material: **203 g**

Free Download: Thingiverse
Search term: "T-Rex Skull"
Designer: "MakerBot"
Downloadlink: https://www.thingiverse.com/thing:308335
Additionally required: ---

* (of 🏆 🏆 🏆 🏆)

5.7.2 Tips on editing and file positioning:

Rotation of all single objects as in the general view in *fig. 50:*

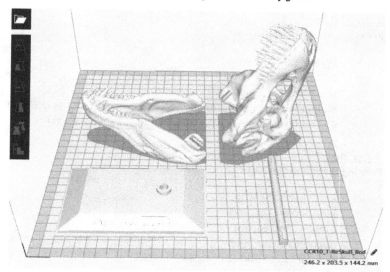

Figure 50: General view of all files to be printed (1x each)

5.7.3 Recommended combination of printing job:

1) "T-RexSkull_Skull" *(color: e.g. white)*
2) "T-RexSkull_Jaw" *(color: e.g. white)*
3) "T-RexSkull_Base" *(color: e.g. grey)*
4) "T-RexSkull_Rod" *(color: e.g. grey)*

5.7.4 Tips on slicing settings for each printing job:

"T-RexSkull_Skull" :
(Printing time: approx. 11 h)

- Layer height: 0.16 mm
- Infill percentage: 20%
- Ironing enabled: no
- **Support structure: yes (Angle: 60°, Percentage: 15 %) as in *fig. 51***

97

- **Bed adhesion: Brim (width: 10 mm; lines: 25; inside: yes)**

"T-RexSkull_Jaw":
(Printing time: approx. 5 h)

- Layer height: 0.16 mm
- Infill percentage: 20%
- Ironing enabled: no
- **Support structure: yes (Angle: 60°, Percentage: 15 %) as in *fig. 51***
- **Bed adhesion: Brim (width: 10 mm; lines: 25; inside: yes)**

„T-Rex_Base":
(Printing time: approx. 5 h)

- Layer height: 0.16 mm
- Infill percentage: 20%
- Ironing enabled: yes
- Support structure: no
- Bed adhesion: Skirt (2 lines, 5 mm offset)

„T-Rex_Rod":
(Printing time: approx. 0.5 h)

- Layer height: 0.16 mm
- Infill percentage: 20%
- Ironing enabled: no
- **Support structure: yes (Angle: 60°, Percentage: 15 %) as in *fig. 51***
- **Bed adhesion: Brim (width: 10 mm; lines: 25; inside: yes)**

5.7.5 Positioning on the printing bed (per print job):

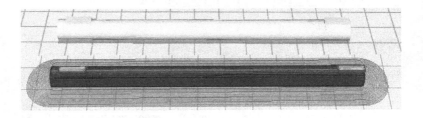

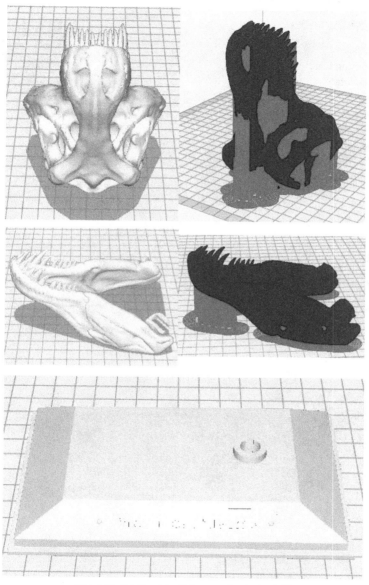

Figure 51: Printing jobs (1 image = 1 printing job)

5.8 Sculpture: Human Skull

5.8.1 Overview:

Difficulty*:
Printing time: 11 h
Material: 245 g

Free Download: Thingiverse
Search term: "Human Skull"
Designer: "MakerBot"
Downloadlink: https://www.thingiverse.com/thing:622390
Additionally required: ---

* (of 🏆 🏆 🏆 🏆)

5.8.2 Tips on editing and file positioning:

Rotation of all single objects as in the general view in *fig. 52*:

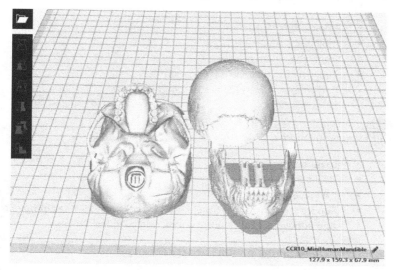

Figure 52: General view of all files to be printed (1x each)

5.8.3 Recommended combination of printing jobs:

3) "MiniHumanSkull1" *(color: e.g. white)*
4) "MiniHumanSkull2" *(color: e.g. white)*
5) "MiniHumanMandible" *(color: e.g. white)*

Scale all parts with a factor of 240% to obtain real human size (optional).

5.8.4 Tips on slicing settings for each printing job:

"MiniHumanSkull1" :
(Printing time: approx. 5 h)

- Layer height: 0.16 mm
- Infill percentage: 25%
- Ironing enabled: no
- Support structure: no
- Bed adhesion: Skirt (2 lines, 5 mm offset)

"MiniHumanSkull2":
(Printing time: approx. 4 h)

- Layer height: 0.16 mm
- Infill percentage: 25%
- Ironing enabled: no
- Support structure: no
- Bed adhesion: Skirt (2 lines, 5 mm offset)

"MiniHumanMandible":
(Printing time: approx. 2 h)

- Layer height: 0.16 mm
- Infill percentage: 25%
- Ironing enabled: no
- **Support structure: yes (Angle: 60°, Percentage: 15 %) as in *fig. 53***
- **Bed adhesion: Brim (width: 8 mm; lines: 20; inside: yes)**

5.8.5 Positioning on the printing bed (per print job):

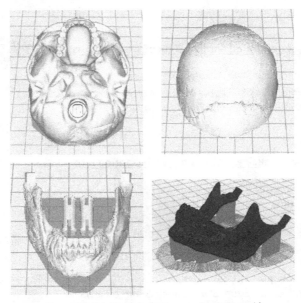

Figure 53: Printing jobs (1 image = 1 printing job)

5.9 Sculpture: Low-Poly-Dog

5.9.1 Overview:

Difficulty*:

Printing time: 3.5 h

Material: 22 g

Free Download: Thingiverse
Search term: "low poly dog"
Designer: "AndrewSink"
Downloadlink: https://www.thingiverse.com/thing:2797399
Additionally required: ---

* (of ⟍⟍⟍⟍)

5.9.2 Tips on editing and file positioning:

Rotation of all single objects as in the general view in *fig. 54:*

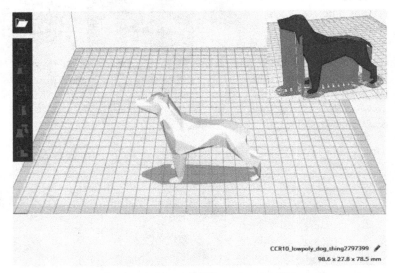

CCR10_lowpoly_dog_thing2797399
98.6 x 27.8 x 78.5 mm

Figure 54: General view of all files to be printed (1x each)

5.9.3 Tips on slicing settings for each printing job:

"Low Poly Dog":
(Printing time: approx. 3.5 h)

- **Color: e.g. white**
- Layer height: 0.16 mm
- Infill percentage: 20%
- Ironing enabled: no
- **Support structure: yes (Angle: 60°, Percentage: 15 %) as in *fig. 54***
- **Bed adhesion: Brim (width: 8 mm; lines: 20; inside: yes)**

5.10 Sculpture: Low-Poly-Horse

5.10.1 Overview:

Difficulty*:   +
Printing time: 6.5 h
Material: 55 g

Free Download: Thingiverse
Search term: "low poly horse"
Designer: "chemlife"
Downloadlink: https://www.thingiverse.com/thing:925638
Additionally required: ---

* (of   )

5.10.2 Tips on editing and file positioning:

Rotation of all single objects as in the general view in *fig. 55:*

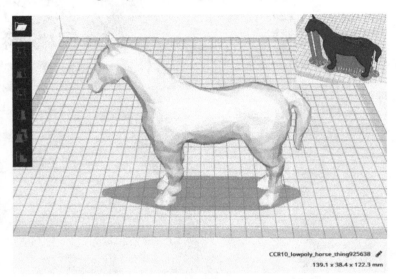

CCR10_lowpoly_horse_thing925638
139.1 x 38.4 x 122.3 mm

Figure 55: General view of all files to be printed (1x each)

5.10.3 Tips on slicing settings for each printing job:

"aaaaaHorse_t2":
(Printing time: approx. 6.5 h)

- **Color: e.g. white**
- Layer height: 0.16 mm
- Infill percentage: 20%
- Ironing enabled: no
- **Support structure: yes (Angle: 60°, Percentage: 15 %) as in *fig. 55***
- **Bed adhesion: Brim (width: 8 mm; lines: 20; inside: yes)**

5.11 Honeycomb-Vase

5.11.1 Overview:

Difficulty*:   +
Printing time: **4 h**
Material: **24 g**

Free Download: Thingiverse
Search term: "honeycomb vase"
Designer: "eggnot"
Downloadlink: https://www.thingiverse.com/thing:2376777
Additionally required: ---

* (of 🏆 🏆 🏆 🏆)

5.11.2 Tips on editing and file positioning:

Rotation of all single objects as in the general view in *fig. 56:*

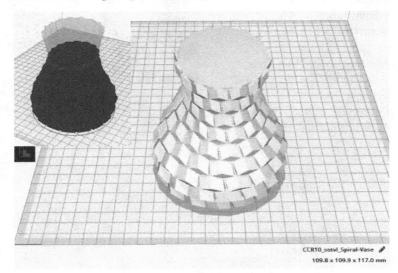

CCR10_sotvl_Spiral-Vase ✏
109.8 x 109.9 x 117.0 mm

Figure 56: General view of all files to be printed (1x each)

5.11.3 Tips on slicing settings for each printing job:

"sotvl Spiral-Vase":
(Printing time: approx. 4 h)

- **Color: e.g. gold**
- Spiralise outer contures (Vase-mode): enabled
- Not waterproof when printed in Vase-mode (for a waterproof version try the other files without printing in vase mode)
- Layer height: 0.12 mm
- Infill Percentage: --
- Ironing enabled: no
- Support structure: no
- Bed adhesion: Skirt (2 lines, 5 mm offset)

6 Toys & Games

6.1 "4 in a row"

6.1.1 Overview:

Difficulty*:
Printing time: **5.5 h**
Material: **33 g**

Free Download: Thingiverse
Search term: "4 in a row"
Designer: "Tibuwi"
Downloadlink: https://www.thingiverse.com/thing:3469041/files
Additionally required: ---

* (of 🏆 🏆 🏆 🏆)

6.1.2 Tips on editing and file positioning:

Rotation of all single objects as in the general view in *fig. 57:*

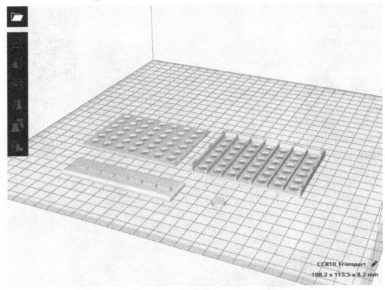

Figure 57: General view of all files to be printed (1x each)

6.1.3 Recommended combination of printing jobs:

1)   "Frontpart" & "Backpart" *(color: e.g. black)*
2)   "Stand" *(color: e.g. black)*
3)   "Gamechips" *(color: e.g. gold & green)*

6.1.4 Tips on slicing settings for each printing job:

"Frontpart" & "Backpart":
(**Printing time: approx. 3.5 h)**

- Layer height: 0.16 mm
- Infill percentage: 20%
- Ironing enabled: yes
- Support structure: no
- Bed adhesion: Skirt (2 lines, 5 mm offset)

"Stand":
(Printing time: approx. 1 h)

- Layer height: 0.16 mm
- Infill percentage: 20%
- Ironing enabled: yes
- Support structure: no
- Bed adhesion: Skirt (2 lines, 5 mm offset)

"Gamechips":
(Printing time: approx. 1 h)

- **Quantitiy: 21 pieces per color**
- Layer height: 0.12 mm
- Infill percentage: 30%
- Ironing enabled: yes
- Support structure: no
- Bed adhesion: Skirt (2 lines, 5 mm offset)

6.1.5 Positioning on the printing bed (per printing job):

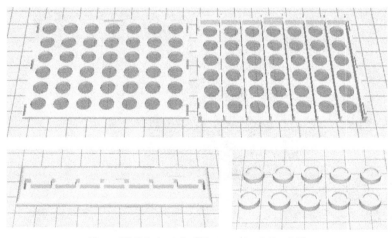

Figure 58: Printing jobs (1 image = 1 printing job)

6.2 Air-Spinner

6.2.1 Overview:

Difficulty*:

Printing time: 3 h

Material: 14 g

Free Download: Thingiverse
Search term: "air spinner"
Designer: "walter"
Downloadlink: https://www.thingiverse.com/thing:2823006
Additionally required: ---

* (of 🏆 🏆 🏆 🏆)

6.2.2 Tips on editing and file positioning:

e.g. "Air_Spinner_2_-_Hollow" as in *fig. 59:*

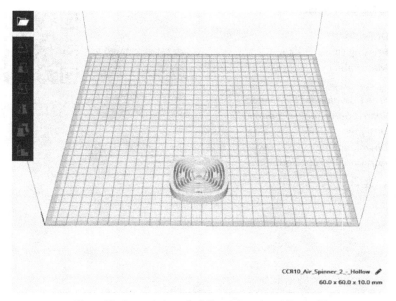

CCR10_Air_Spinner_2_-_Hollow ✏
60.0 x 60.0 x 10.0 mm

Figure 59: General view of all files to be printed (1x each)

6.2.3 Tips on slicing settings for each printing job:

"Air Spinner 2 - Hollow ":
(Printing time: approx. 3 h)

- **Color: e.g. blue**
- Layer height: 0.12 mm
- Infill percentage: 20%
- Ironing enabled: yes
- Support structure: no
- Bed adhesion: Skirt (2 lines, 5 mm offset)

6.3 Puzzle: Animals

6.3.1 Overview:

Difficulty*:
Printing time: **5.5 h**
Material: **53 g**

Free Download: Thingiverse
Search term: "animals puzzle"
Designer: "guss67"
Downloadlink: https://www.thingiverse.com/thing:2777352
Additionally required: ---

* (of   )

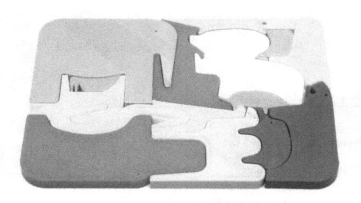

6.3.2 Tips on editing and file positioning:

Positioning of all single objects as in the general view in *fig. 60:*

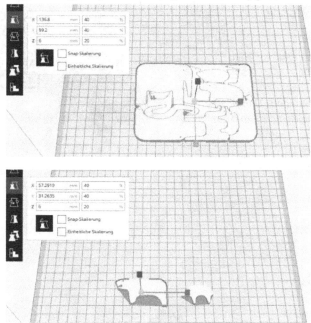

Figure 60: General view of all files to be printed (1x each)

6.3.3 Tips on slicing settings for each printing job:

"animals puzzle" (one color for all) or each animal single (multi-colored):
(Printing time: for all approx. 5.5 h)

- **Color: different colors for each animal (or two animals) or one color for all**
- Scale all animals (x: 40% , y: 40%, z: 20%) for faster printing (z) and a smaller size (x, y) (optional)
- Layer height: 0.16 mm
- Infill percentage: 25%
- Ironing enabled: yes
- Support structure: no
- Bed adhesion: Skirt (2 lines, 5 mm offset)

6.4 Gordian Knot

6.4.1 Overview:

Difficulty*:
Printing time: **4.5 h**
Material: **45 g**

Free Download: Thingiverse
Search term: "gordian knot"
Designer: "Lenbok"
Downloadlink: https://www.thingiverse.com/thing:11204
Additionally required: ---

* (of 🏆 🏆 🏆 🏆)

6.4.2 Tips on editing and file positioning:

Positioning of all single objects as in the general view in *fig. 61*:

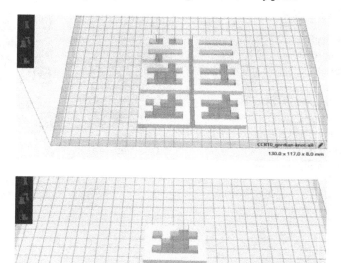

Figure 61: General view of all files to be printed (1x each)

6.4.3 Tips on slicing settings for each printing job:

"gordian-knot-all" *(one color for all) or each object single (multi-colored):*
(Printing time: approx. 5.5 h for all)

- **Color: different colors for each object (or two objects) or one color for all**
- Layer height: 0.16 mm
- Infill percentage: 20%
- Ironing enabled: yes
- Support structure: no
- Bed adhesion: Skirt (2 lines, 5 mm offset)

117

6.5 Board Game: Wobbly Chess

6.5.1 Overview:

Difficulty*:	🏆🏆🏆🏆 +
Printing time:	**90 h**
Material:	**1100 g**

Free Download: Thingiverse
Search term: "wobbly chess"
Designer: "MikeyB"
Downloadlink: https://www.thingiverse.com/thing:53604
Additionally required: ---

* (of 🏆🏆🏆🏆)

6.5.2 Tips on slicing settings for each printing job:

Rotation of all single objects as in the general view in *fig. 62:*

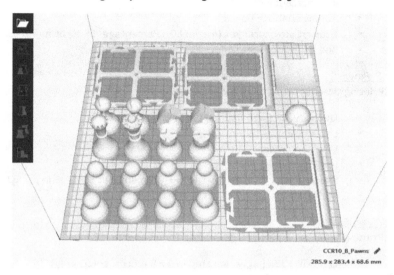

Figure 62: General view of all files to be printed (more times each)

6.5.3 Recommended combination of printing jobs:

1) "Pieces_x_8_support" (figures) *(2x; e.g. 1x black & 1x white)*
2) "8_Pawns" (pawns) *(2x; e.g. 1x black & 1x white)*
3) "Piece_Base" *(32x; e.g. grey)*
4) "Board_Square_x_4 " *(16x; 8x black & 8x white)*
5) "Board_Center" *(4x; e.g. green)*
6) "Board_Corner" *(4x; e.g. green)*
7) "Board_Edge" *(8x; e.g. green)*

6.5.4 Tips on slicing settings for each printing job:

"Pieces_x_8_support" (figure without pawns):
(Printing time: approx. 5.5 h; for all approx. 11 h)

- Print file „knight" as the two-part version & glue it together
- **Quantity: 2x (= 16 figures) (1x black, 1x white)**

119

- Layer height: 0.16 mm
- Infill percentage: 20%
- Ironing enabled: no
- **Support structure: yes (Angle: 60°, Percentage: 15 %) as in *fig.* 63**
- Bed adhesion: Skirt (2 lines, 5 mm offset)

"8 Pawns":
(Printing time: approx. 4.5 h; for all approx. 9 h)

- **Quantity: 2x (= 16 figures) (1x black, 1x white)**
- Layer height: 0.16 mm
- Infill percentage: 20%
- Ironing enabled: no
- **Support structure: yes (Angle: 60°, Percentage: 15 %) as in *fig.* 63**
- Bed adhesion: Skirt (2 lines, 5 mm offset)

"Piece Base":
(Printing time: per 8 pieces approx. 3 h; for all approx. 12 h)

- **Quantity: 32x (e.g. separated in 4 x 8 pieces; color: grey)**
- Layer height: 0.16 mm
- Infill percentage: 20%
- Ironing enabled: no
- **Support structure: yes (Angle: 60°, Percentage: 15 %) as in *fig.* 63**
- Bed adhesion: Skirt (2 lines, 5 mm offset)

"Board Square x 4":
(Printing time: per 16 pieces approx. 9.5 h; for all approx. 38 h)

- **Quantity: 64x (e.g. separated in 4 x 16 pieces; color: 32 black, 32 white)**
- Layer height: 0.2 mm
- Infill percentage: 20%
- Ironing enabled: no
- Support structure: no
- Bed adhesion: Skirt (2 lines, 5 mm offset)

"Board Center":
(Printing time: per 2 pieces approx. 2 h; for all approx. 4 h)

- **Quantity: 4x (e.g. separated in 2 x 2 pieces; color: e.g. green)**
- Layer height: 0.2 mm

- Infill percentage: 20%
- Ironing enabled: no
- Support structure: no
- Bed adhesion: Skirt (2 lines, 5 mm offset)

"Board Corner":
(Printing time: per 2 pieces approx. 3 h; for all approx. 6 h)

- **Quantity: 4x (e.g. separated in 2 x 2 pieces; color: e.g. green)**
- Layer height: 0.2 mm
- Infill percentage: 20%
- Ironing enabled: no
- Support structure: no
- Bed adhesion: Skirt (2 lines, 5 mm offset)

"Board Edge":
(Printing time: per 2 pieces approx. 2.5 h; for all 10 h)

- **Quantity: 8x (e.g. separated in 4 x 2 pieces; color: e.g. green)**
- Layer height: 0.2 mm
- Infill percentage: 20%
- Ironing enabled: no
- Support structure: no
- Bed adhesion: Skirt (2 lines, 5 mm offset)

6.5.6 Positioning on the printing bed (per print job):

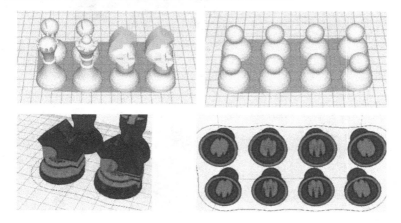

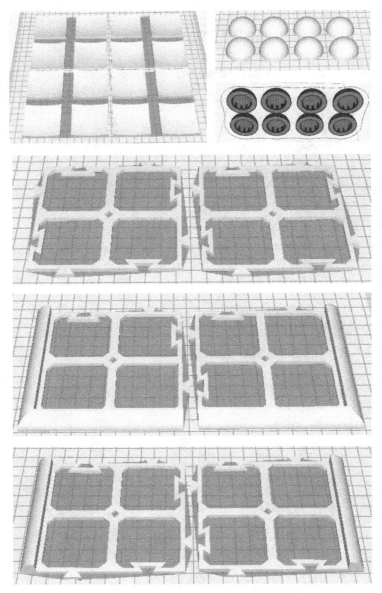

Figure 63: Printing jobs (1 image = 1 printing job)

6.6 Toy: Airplane

6.6.1 Overview:

Difficulty*: 🏆 🏆 +

Printing time: **6 h**

Material: **79 g**

Free Download: Thingiverse
Search term: "toy plane bolts"
Designer: "PlasilABS"
Downloadlink: *https://www.thingiverse.com/thing:1642670*
Additionally required: ---

* (of 🏆 🏆 🏆 🏆)

6.6.2 Tips on editing and file positioning:

Rotation of all single objects as in the general view in *fig. 64:*

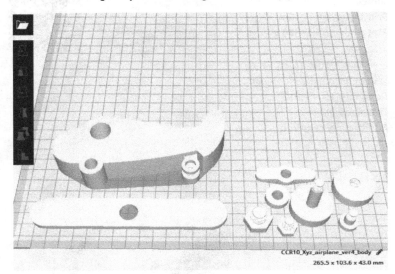

Figure 64: General view of all files to be printed (1x each)

6.6.3 Recommended combination of printing jobs:

1) "Xyz_airplane_ver4_body" *(color: e.g. blue)*
2) "Xyz_airplane_ver4_wing" *(color: e.g. black)*
3) **Single parts:** "Xyz_airplane_ver4_prop_bolt" &
   "Xyz_airplane_ver4_propeller" & "Xyz_airplane_ver4_rear_bolt" &
   "Xyz_airplane_ver4_rear_wheel" & "Xyz_airplane_ver4_wheel_Left" &
   "Xyz_airplane_ver4_wheel_Right" & "Xyz_airplane_ver4_wing_bolt"
   (color: e.g. black)

6.6.4 Tips on slicing settings for each printing job:

"Xyz_airplane_ver4_body ":
(**Printing time: approx. 4 h**)

- Layer height: 0.16 mm
- Infill percentage: 20%
- Ironing enabled: yes
- **Support structure: yes (Angle: 60°, Percentage: 15 %) as in *fig. 65***
- Bed adhesion: Skirt (2 lines, 5 mm offset)

"Xyz_airplane_ver4_wing":
(**Printing time: approx. 1 h**)

- Layer height: 0.16 mm
- Infill percentage: 20%
- Ironing enabled: yes
- Support structure: no
- Bed adhesion: Skirt (2 lines, 5 mm offset)

Single Parts (3):
(**Printing time: approx. 1 h**)

- Layer height: 0.16 mm
- Infill percentage: 20%
- Ironing enabled: yes
- Support structure: no
- Bed adhesion: Skirt (2 lines, 5 mm offset)

6.6.5 Positioning on the printing bed (per print job):

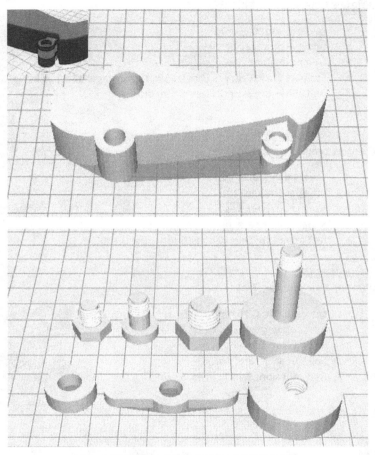

Figure 65: Printing jobs (1 image = 1 printing job)

7 Storage

7.1 SD-Card Storage

7.1.1 Overview:

Difficulty*:
Printing time: ca. 2,5 h
Material: ca. 8 g

Free Download: Thingiverse
Search term: "parametric sd card"
Designer: "bikecyclist"
Downloadlink: https://www.thingiverse.com/thing:3470191
Additionally required: ---

* (of 🏆 🏆 🏆 🏆)

7.1.2 Tips on editing and file positioning:

Positioning of all single objects as in the general view in *fig. 66:*

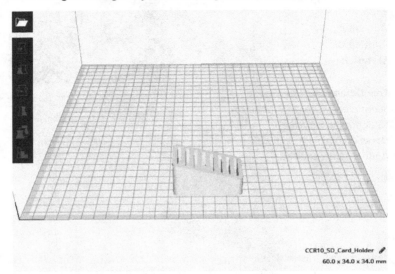

CCR10_SD_Card_Holder
60.0 x 34.0 x 34.0 mm

Figure 66: General view of all files to be printed (1x each)

7.1.3 Tips on slicing settings for each printing job:

"SD Card Holder":
(Printing time: approx. 2.5 h)

- **Color: e.g. black**
- Layer height: 0.16 mm
- Infill percentage: 20%
- Ironing enabled: no
- Support structure: no
- Bed adhesion: Skirt (2 lines, 5 mm offset)

7.2 Towel Hook

7.2.1 Overview:

Difficulty*:
Printing time: 2,5 h
Material: 6 g

Free Download: Thingiverse
Search term: "towel hook"
Designer: "bradk2012"
Downloadlink: https://www.thingiverse.com/thing:32408
Additionally required: ---

* (of 🏆 🏆 🏆 🏆)

7.2.2 Tips on editing and file positioning:

Positioning of all single objects as in the general view in *fig. 67:*

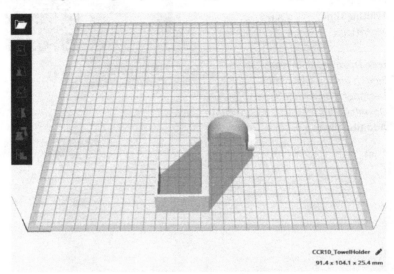

CCR10_TowelHolder
91.4 x 104.1 x 25.4 mm

Figure 67: General view of all files to be printed (1x each)

7.2.3 Tips on slicing settings for each printing job:

"TowelHolder":

(Printing time: approx. 2.5 h)

- **Color: e.g. black**
- Layer height: 0.16 mm
- Infill percentage: 50%
- Ironing enabled: yes
- Support structure: no
- Bed adhesion: Skirt (2 lines, 5 mm offset)

7.3 Bag Hooks

7.3.1 Overview:

Difficulty*:
Printing time: **5 h**
Material: **16 g**

***Free Download:** Thingiverse*
Search term: "seatback bag hooks"
Designer: "YoungBuck"
Downloadlink: https://www.thingiverse.com/thing:128136
Additionally required: ---

* (of 🏆 🏆 🏆 🏆)

7.3.2 Tips on editing and file positioning:

Positioning of all single objects as in the general view in *fig. 68:*

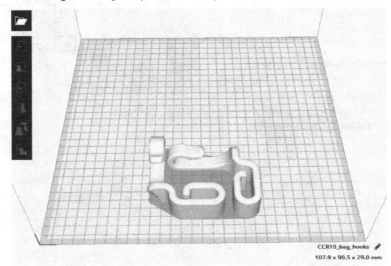

CCR10_bag_hooks
107.9 x 90.5 x 29.0 mm

Figure 68: General view of all files to be printed (1x each)

7.3.3 Tips on slicing settings for each printing job:

"bag hooks norkless":
(Printing time: approx. 5 h)

- **Color: e.g. black**
- Layer height: 0.16 mm
- Infill percentage: 40%
- Ironing enabled: no
- **Support structure: yes (Angle: 60°, Percentage: 15 %) as in *fig. 69***
- Bed adhesion: Skirt (2 lines, 5 mm offset)

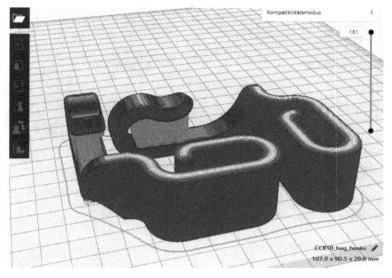

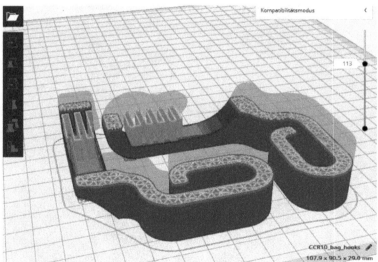

Abbildung 69: Printing job (Layerview)

7.4 Bowl

7.4.1 Overview:

Difficulty*:
Printing time: **7 h**
Material: **59 g**

Free Download: Thingiverse
Search term: "basket bowl"
Designer: "Robine"
Downloadlink: https://www.thingiverse.com/thing:2852321
Additionally required: ---

* (of 🏆 🏆 🏆 🏆)

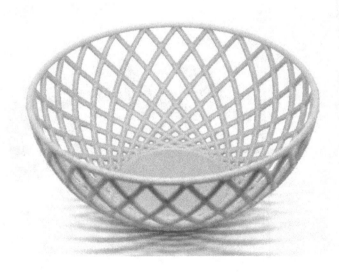

7.4.2 Tips on editing and file positioning:

"basket_bowl" as in *fig. 70:*

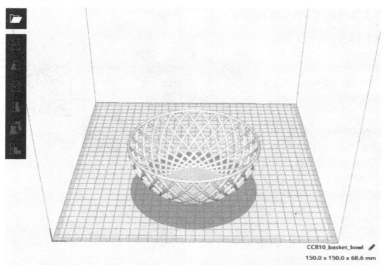

CCR10_basket_bowl 🖊
150.0 x 150.0 x 68.6 mm

Figure 70: General view of all files to be printed (1x each)

7.4.3 Tips on slicing settings for each printing job:

"basket_bowl":
(Printing time: approx. 7 h)

- **Color: e.g. gold**
- Layer height: 0.2 mm
- Infill percentage: 25%
- Ironing enabled: no
- Support structure: no
- Bed adhesion: Skirt (2 lines, 5 mm offset)

8 Tool-Accessories

8.1 Driller Dust Container

8.1.1 Overview:

Difficulty*:

Printing time: 5.5 h

Material: 46 g

Free Download: Thingiverse
Search term: "driller dust proof"
Designer: "celiktse"
Downloadlink: https://www.thingiverse.com/thing:3368270
Additionally required: ---

* (of 🦷🦷🦷🦷)

8.1.2 Tips on editing and file positioning:

Positioning of all single objects as in the general view in *fig. 71*:

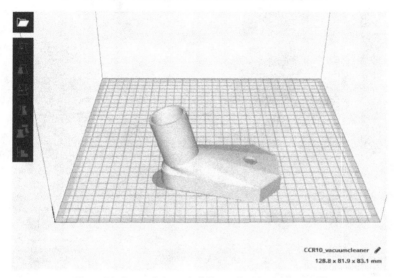

Figure 71: General view of all files to be printed (1x each)

8.1.3 Tips on slicing settings for each printing job:

"vacuumcleaner":
(Printing time: ca. 5,5 h)

- **Color: e.g. black**
- Layer height: 0.16 mm
- Infill percentage: 20%
- Ironing enabled: no
- **Support structure: yes (Angle: 60°, Percentage: 15 %) as in *fig. 72***
- Bed adhesion: Brim (width: 6 mm; lines: 15; inside: yes)

8.1.4 Support structure:

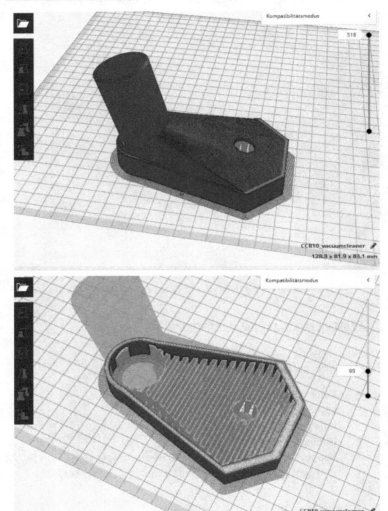

Abbildung 72: Support structure (Layer view)

8.2 Pliers Stand

8.2.1 Overview:

Difficulty*:

Printing time: **5.5 h**

Material: **52 g**

Free Download: Thingiverse
Search term: "pliers stand"
Designer: "arhis"
Downloadlink: *https://www.thingiverse.com/thing:2572892*
Additionally required: ---

* (of)

8.2.2 Tips on editing and file positioning:

Rotation of all single objects as in the general view in *fig. 73:*

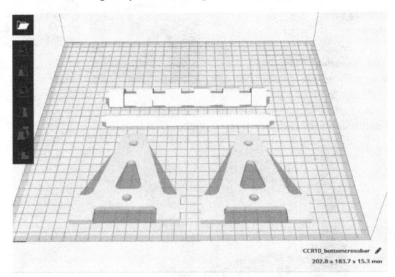

CCR10_bottomcrossbar
202.8 x 183.7 x 15.3 mm

Figure 73: General view of all files to be printed (1x each)

8.2.3 Recommended combination of printing jobs:

1)   "side" *(color: e.g. black)*
2)   "bottomcrossbar" & "uppercrossbar" *(color: e.g. black)*

8.2.4 Tips on slicing settings for each printing job:

"side":
(Printing time: approx. 3 h)

- **Quantity: 2 pieces (one printing job)**
- Layer height: 0.16 mm
- Scale the sides (x: 100% , y: 100%, z: 70%) for a faster printing time (z) (optional)
- Ironing enabled: yes
- Support structure: no

- Bed adhesion: Skirt (2 lines, 5 mm offset)

"bottomcrossbar" & "uppercrossbar":
(Printing time: approx. 2.5 h)

- Layer height: 0.16 mm
- Infill percentage: 25%
- Ironing enabled: no
- **Support structure: yes (Angle: 60°, Percentage: 15 %) as in fig. 74**
- Bed adhesion: Skirt (2 lines, 5 mm offset)

8.2.5 Positioning on the printing bed (per printing job):

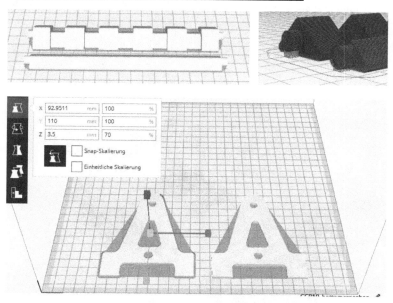

Figure 74: Printing jobs (1 image = 1 printing job)

Maybe you have to widen the drilling holes of the sides (e.g. use a drill). This depends on your 3D printer´s accuracy.

8.3 Machine Vise

8.3.1 Overview:

Difficulty*:   ☐ ☐ ☐ +
Printing time: 19.5 h
Material: 166 g

Free Download: Thingiverse
Search term: "machine vise"
Designer: "TheGoofy"
Downloadlink: https://www.thingiverse.com/thing:2064269
Additionally required: ---

* (of ☐ ☐ ☐ ☐)

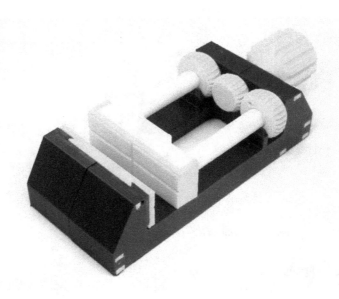

8.3.2 Tips on editing and file positioning:

Rotation of all single objects as in the general view in *fig. 75:*

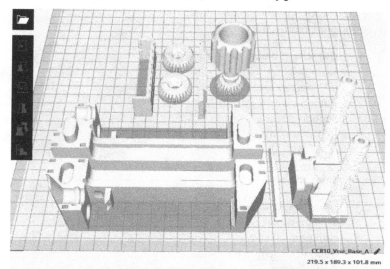

CCR10_Vise_Base_A
219.5 x 189.3 x 101.8 mm

Figure 75: General view of all files to be printed (1x each)

8.3.3 Recommended combination of printing jobs:

1) "Vise_Base_A" & "Vise_Base_B" *(color: e.g. black)*
2) 7x "Vise_Base_Clip" *(color: e.g. green)*
3) "Vise_Base_Jaw_Plate" *(color: e.g. green)*
4) "Vise_Handle" & 2x "Vise_Main_Gear" & "Vise_Sliding_Jaw" & "Vise_Sliding_Jaw_Plate" *(color: e.g. white)*

8.3.4 Tips on slicing settings for each printing job:

"Vise_Base_A" & "Vise_Base_B" :
(Printing time: approx. 10 h)

- Layer height: 0.16 mm
- Infill percentage: 25%
- Ironing enabled: yes
- Support structure: no

143

- Bed adhesion: Skirt (2 lines, 5 mm offset)

"Vise Base Clip":
(Printing time: approx. 0.5 h)

- **Quantity: 7 pieces (one printing job)**
- Layer height: 0.16 mm
- Infill percentage: 25%
- Ironing enabled: yes
- Support structure: no
- Bed adhesion: Skirt (2 lines, 5 mm offset)

"Vise Base Jaw Plate":
(Printing time: approx. 4 h)

- Layer height: 0.16 mm
- Infill percentage: 25%
- Ironing enabled: yes
- Support structure: no
- Bed adhesion: Skirt (2 lines, 5 mm offset)

"Vise Handle" & 2x "Vise Main Gear" & "Vise Sliding Jaw" &
"Vise Sliding Jaw Plate":
(Printing time: approx. 5 h)

- Layer height: 0.16 mm
- Infill percentage: 25%
- Ironing enabled: yes
- Support structure: no
- Bed adhesion: Skirt (2 lines, 5 mm offset)

8.3.5 Positioning on the printing bed (per print job):

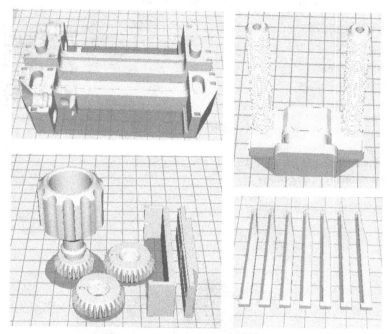

Figure 76: Printing jobs (1 image = 1 printing job)

8.3.6 Assembly:

Video:

https://youtu.be/mziT7KV-fRI or click on the Thingiverse link (p. 142).

8.4 Platform Jack (printed fully assembled)

8.4.1 Overview:

Difficulty*:

Printing time: **12 h**

Material: **77 g**

Free Download: Thingiverse
Search term: "platform jack"
Designer: "Intentional3D"
Downloadlink: *https://www.thingiverse.com/thing:925556*
Additionally required: ---

* (of)

8.4.2 Tips on editing and file positioning:

Rotation of all single objects as in the general view in *fig. 77:*

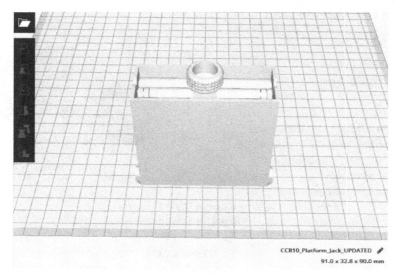

CCR10_Platform_Jack_UPDATED
91.0 x 32.8 x 90.0 mm

Figure 77: General view of all files to be printed (1x each)

8.4.3 Tips on slicing settings for each printing job:

"Platform_Jack_UPDATED":
(**Printing time: approx. 12 h**)

- **Color: e.g. black**
- Layer height: 0.2 mm
- Infill percentage: 20%
- Ironing enabled: no
- Support structure: no
- Bed adhesion: Skirt (2 lines, 5 mm offset)

Be cautios when using it the first time. Loosen the parts first!

9 Complex Objects (fully functional)

9.1 Mechanical Clock

9.1.1 Overview:

Difficulty*:	♟ ♟ ♟ ♟ ♟ +
Printing time:	26.5 h
Material:	185 g

Free Download: Thingiverse
Search term: "mechanical clock"
Designer: "TheGoofy"
Downloadlink: https://www.thingiverse.com/thing:328569

Additionally required:

- Bolts: 6 pieces M3x12 (flat-head)
             5 pieces M3x10 (flat-head)
- Pins: 1 x 1,5 mm x 40 mm *(Quantity / Ø / Length)*
             1 x 2,0 mm x 28 mm | 1 x 3,0 mm x 30 mm

* (of ♟ ♟ ♟ ♟ ♟)   1 x 2,0 mm x 60 mm | 4 x 3,0 mm x 39 mm
             2 x 3,0 mm x 60 mm | 1 x 3,0 mm x 15 mm

9.1.2 Recommended combination of printing jobs:

1) **Gears:** "Crank_Gear_Reduction"; "Gear_Reduction_Minutes_...";
   "Gear_Reduction_Seconds_..."; "Gear_Wheel_Hours";
   "Gear_Wheel_Minutes"; "Gear_Wheel_Seconds";
   "Winding_Gear_Crank"; "Winding_Gear_Pawl";
   "Winding_Gear_Transmission"; "Winding_Planet_Ring_Gear_v1";
   "Winding_Planet_Sun_Gear_for_Crank"; "Winding Planets";

2) **Escapement:** "Escapement_Spring"; "Escapement_Anchor";
   "Escapement_Balance"; "Escapement_Wheel";

3) **Winding:** "Winding_Drum_with_Ratchet";
   "Winding_Planet_Carrier_Cover"; "Winding_Planet_Carrier_Drum";
   "Winding_Planet_Crank_Shaft_Gear"; "Winding_Planet_Pawl";
   "Winding_Planet_Roller_Bearing";

4) **Weight:** "Weight_Pulley_A"; "Weight_Pulley_B"; "Weight_Pulley
   Hook" (siehe auch Details unten)

5) **Frame:** "Frame_Back"; "Frame_Cord_Mount"; "Frame_Front"

6) **Crank:** "Crank_Handle"; "Crank_Handle_Screw"; "Crank_Shaft"; &
   Clock_Face_Hand: "Clock_Face_Hand_Hour";
   "Clock_Face_Hand_Minute"; "Clock_Face_Hand_Second"

7) "Clock_Face_Background"

8) "Clock_Face_Tickmarks"

9.1.3 Tips on slicing settings for each printing job:

Gears (1):
(Printing time: approx. 10.5 h)

- Layer height: 0.2 mm
- ***Color: e.g. black***
- Infill percentage: 25%
- Ironing enabled: no
- Support structure: no
- Bed adhesion: Skirt (2 lines, 5 mm offset)

Escapement (2):
(Printing time: approx. 2 h)

- Layer height: 0.2 mm
- ***Color: e.g. green***

- Infill percentage: 25%
- Ironing enabled: no
- Support structure: no
- Bed adhesion: Skirt (2 lines, 5 mm offset)

Winding (3):
(Printing time: approx. 4 h)

- Layer height: 0.2 mm
- ***Color: e.g. gold***
- Infill percentage: 25%
- Ironing enabled: no
- Support structure: no
- Bed adhesion: Skirt (2 lines, 5 mm offset)

Weight (4):
(Printing time: approx. 0.5 h)

- Layer height: 0.2 mm
- ***Color: e.g. green***
- Infill percentage: 25%
- Ironing enabled: no
- Support structure: no
- Bed adhesion: Skirt (2 lines, 5 mm offset)

"Weight_Bucket" & "Weight_Bucket Cover" are not listed here, because a simple weight with an eyelet will be used instead. Depending on variants, several parts listed here will remain unused or do not have to be printed. For further instructions and assembly hints, watch the designer's video (Thingiverse link p. 148).

Frame (5):
(Printing time: approx. 6 h)

- Layer height: 0.2 mm
- ***Color: e.g. black***
- Infill percentage: 25%
- Ironing enabled: no
- Support structure: no
- Bed adhesion: Skirt (2 lines, 5 mm offset)

Crank & Clock Face Hand (6):
(Printing time: approx. 1.5 h)

- Layer height: 0.2 mm
- ***Color: e.g. gold***
- Infill percentage: 25%
- Ironing enabled: no
- Support structure: no
- Bed adhesion: Skirt (2 lines, 5 mm offset)

„Clock Face Background" (7):
(Printing time: approx. 1 h)

- Layer height: 0.2 mm
- ***Color: e.g. grey***
- Infill percentage: 25%
- Ironing enabled: no
- Support structure: no
- Bed adhesion: Skirt (2 lines, 5 mm offset)

„Clock Face Tickmarks" (8):
(Printing time: approx. 1 h)

- Layer height: 0.2 mm
- ***Color: e.g. green***
- Infill percentage: 25%
- Ironing enabled: no
- Support structure: no
- Bed adhesion: Skirt (2 lines, 5 mm offset)

9.1.4 Positioning on the printing bed (per print job):

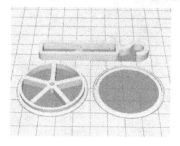

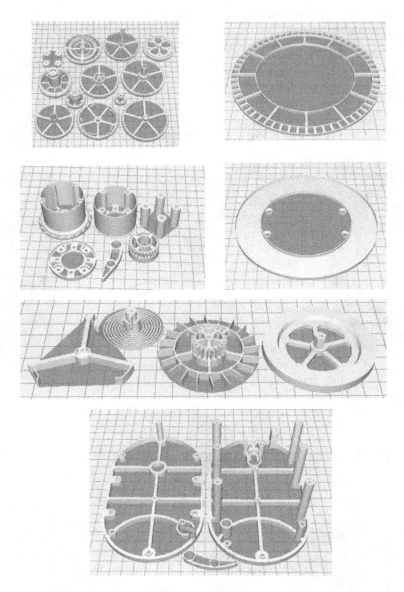

Figure 78: Printing jobs (1 image = 1 printing job)

9.2 Luxo Jr. Lamp (Pixar)

9.2.1 Overview:

Difficulty*:
Printing time: 35 h
Material: 431 g

Free Download: Thingiverse
Search term: "large luxo jr"
Designer: "DanielBull"
Downloadlink: https://www.thingiverse.com/thing:432648
Additionally required: several springs and a flashlight

* (of 🏆 🏆 🏆 🏆)

9.2.2 Tips on editing and file positioning:

Rotation of all single objects as in the general view in *fig. 79:*

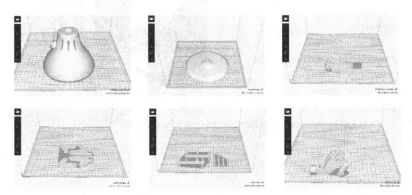

Figure 79: Printing jobs (1 image = 1 printing job)

9.2.3 Recommended combination of printing jobs:

1) "lamp_bell"*(e.g. white)*
2) "base" *(e.g. white)*
3) "box_sections" *(e.g. white)*
4) "hinges"*(e.g. white)*
5) "links" & "rods" *(e.g. white)*
6) "neck" & "stem" *(e.g. white)*

9.2.4 Tips on slicing settings for each printing job:

"lamp_bell":
(Printing time: approx. 12,5 h)

- Layer height: 0.16 mm
- Infill percentage: 20%
- Ironing enabled: yes
- **Support structure: yes (Angle: 60°, Percentage: 15 %) as in *fig. 80***
- **Bed adhesion: Brim (width: 6 mm; lines: 15; inside: yes)**

"base":
(Printing time: approx. 10 h)

- Layer height: 0.16 mm
- Infill percentage: 25%
- Ironing enabled: yes
- Support structure: no
- Bed adhesion: Skirt (2 lines, 5 mm offset)

"box sections":
(Printing time: approx. 3 h)

- Layer height: 0.16 mm
- Infill percentage: 35%
- Ironing enabled: yes
- Support structure: no
- Bed adhesion: Skirt (2 lines, 5 mm offset)

"hinges":
(Printing time: approx. 3 h)

- Layer height: 0.16 mm
- Infill percentage: 35%
- Ironing enabled: yes
- Support structure: no
- Bed adhesion: Skirt (2 lines, 5 mm offset)

"links" & "rods":
(Printing time: approx. 2,5 h)

- Layer height: 0.16 mm
- Infill percentage: 40%
- Ironing enabled: yes
- Support structure: no
- Bed adhesion: Skirt (2 lines, 5 mm offset)

"neck" & "stem":
(Printing time: approx. 4 h)

- Layer height: 0.16 mm
- Infill percentage: 50%

- Ironing enabled: yes
- Support structure: no
- Bed adhesion: Skirt (2 lines, 5 mm offset)

9.2.5 Positioning on the printing bed (per print job):

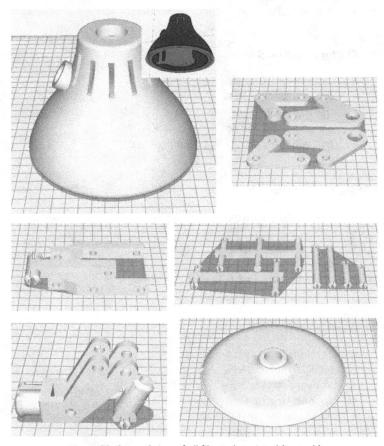

Figure 80: General view of all files to be printed (1x each)

10 Fun & Other

10.1 Cryptex

10.1.1 Overview:

Difficulty*:
Printing time: **34 h**
Material: **307 g**

Free Download: Thingiverse
Search term: "10 letter cryptex"
Designer: "MasonStonehenge"
Downloadlink: *https://www.thingiverse.com/thing:3074829*
Additionally required: ---

* (of 🖶 🖶 🖶 🖶)

10.1.2 Tips on editing and file positioning:

Rotation of all single objects as in the general view in *fig. 81:*

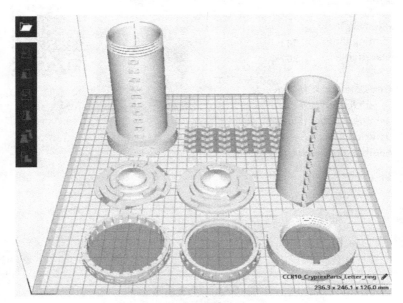

Figure 81: General view of all files to be printed (1x each)

10.1.3 Recommended combination of printing jobs:

1) "Outer Core" & "Inner Core" *(color: e.g. gold)*
2) "Letter rings" 10x *(color: e.g. grey)*
3) "Letter encoding rings" *(color: e.g. grey)*
4) "Outer Core decorative top" & "Inner Core decorative top" & "Outer Core retainer"*(color: e.g. gold)*
5) "Springs"*(color: e.g. grey)*

10.1.4 Tips on slicing settings for each printing job:

"Outer Core" & "Inner Core":
(Printing time: approx. 10.5 h)

- Layer height: 0.16 mm
- Infill percentage: 20%
- Ironing enabled: no
- Support structure: no
- Bed adhesion: Brim (width: 8 mm; lines: 20; inside: yes)

"Letter rings":
(Printing time: approx. 11 h for all)

- **Quantity: 10 pieces (5 per printing job)**
- Layer height: 0.16 mm
- Infill percentage: 20%
- Ironing enabled: no
- Support structure: no
- Bed adhesion: Skirt (2 lines, 5 mm offset)

"Letter encoding rings":
(Printing time: approx. 7 h for all)

- **Quantity: 10 pieces (5 per printing job)**
- Layer height: 0.16 mm
- Infill percentage: 20%
- Ironing enabled: no
- Support structure: no
- Bed adhesion: Brim (width: 8 mm; lines: 20; inside: yes)

"Outer Core decorative top" & "Inner Core decorative top" & "Outer Core retainer":
(Printing time: approx. 5 h for all)

- Layer height: 0.16 mm
- Infill percentage: 20%
- Ironing enabled: yes
- Support structure: no
- Bed adhesion: Skirt (2 lines, 5 mm offset)

„Springs":
(Printing time: approx. 0.5 h for all)

- **Quantity: 30 pieces (one printing job)**
- Layer height: 0.16 mm
- Infill percentage: 40%
- Ironing enabled: yes
- Support structure: no
- Bed adhesion: Brim (width: 4 mm; lines: 10; inside: yes)

10.1.5 Positioning on the printing bed (per print job):

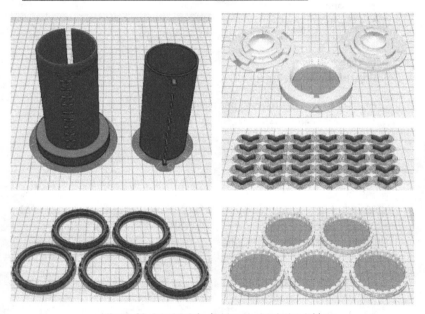

Figure 82: Printing jobs (1 image = 1 printing job)

Assembly: When putting together the springs, the body parts and the rings you may have to use a little bit of force and/or a tool (hammer, plier). Be cautious when doing this! Maybe downscale or upscale the parts by 1% for a better fit.

10.2 Bee Hotel

10.2.1 Overview:

Difficulty*:

Printing time: **5 h**

Material: **49 g**

Free Download: Thingiverse
Search term: "bee hotel"
Designer: "godorowski"
Downloadlink: <u>https://www.thingiverse.com/thing:3052138</u>
Additionally required: a screw

* (of 🏆 🏆 🏆 🏆)

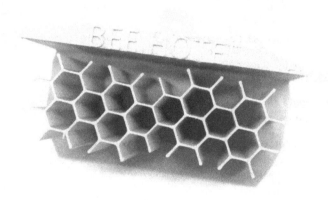

10.2.2 Tips on editing and file positioning:

"Bee_Hotel" as in *fig. 83:*

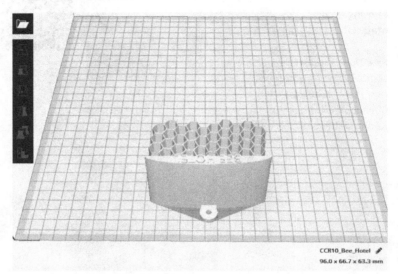

CCR10_Bee_Hotel
96.0 x 66.7 x 63.3 mm

Figure 83: General view of all files to be printed (1x each)

10.2.3 Tips on slicing settings for each printing job:

"Bee_Hotel":
(Printing time: approx. 5 h)

- **color: e.g. gold**
- Layer height: 0.2 mm
- Infill percentage: 20%
- Ironing enabled: yes
- Support structure: no
- Bed adhesion: Skirt (2 lines, 5 mm offset)

10.3 Butterfly (articulated)

10.3.1 Overview:

Difficulty*:
Printing time: **4 h**
Material: **28 g**

Free Download: Thingiverse
Search term: "articulated butterfly"
Designer: "8ran"
Downloadlink: <u>https://www.thingiverse.com/thing:2810756</u>
Additionally required: ---

* (of 🌱 🌱 🌱 🌱)

10.3.2 Tips on editing and file positioning:

Positioning of all single objects as in the general view in *fig. 84:*

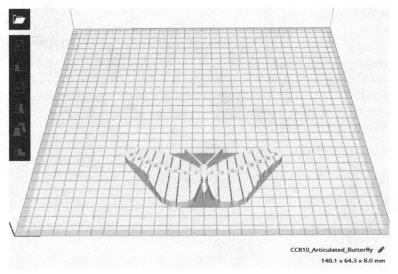

CCR10_Articulated_Butterfly
140.1 x 64.3 x 8.0 mm

Figure 84: General view of all files to be printed (1x each)

10.3.3 Tips on slicing settings for each printing job:

"Articulated Butterfly":
(**Printing time: approx. 4 h**)

- **Color: e.g. gold**
- Layer height: 0.16 mm
- Infill percentage: 20%
- Ironing enabled: yes
- Support structure: no
- Bed adhesion: Skirt (2 lines, 5 mm offset)

10.4 Present Ornament (lockable)

10.4.1 Overview:

Difficulty*:
Printing time: 11.5 h
Material: 86 g

Free Download: Thingiverse
Search term: "lockable present"
Designer: "jijimath"
Downloadlink: https://www.thingiverse.com/thing:191974
Additionally required: ---

* (of 🏆 🏆 🏆 🏆)

10.4.2 Tips on editing and file positioning:

Rotation of all single objects as in the general view in *fig. 85:*

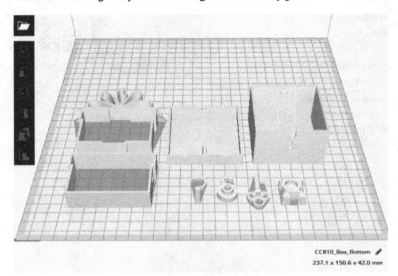

CCR10_Box_Bottom
237.1 x 150.6 x 42.0 mm

Figure 85: General view of all files to be printed (1x each)

10.4.3 Recommended combination of printing jobs:

1)   "Box_Bottom" & "Box_Lid" *(color: e.g. gold)*
2)   "Branch_Hook" & "key" & "Lock_Clasp" & "Lock_Socket" *(color: e.g. grey)*
3)   "Ribbon_Part_1" & "Ribbon_Part_2" *(color: e.g. red)*

10.4.4 Tips on slicing settings for each printing job:

"Box_Bottom" & "Box_Lid":
(Printing time: approx. 6.5 h)

- Layer height: 0.16 mm
- Infill percentage: 20%
- Ironing enabled: yes
- Support structure: no
- Bed adhesion: Skirt (2 lines, 5 mm offset)

"Branch Hook" & "key" & "Lock Clasp" & "Lock Socket":
(Printing time: approx. 1 h)

- Layer height: 0.16 mm
- Infill percentage: 70%
- Ironing enabled: yes
- **Support structure: yes (Angle: 60°, Percentage: 15 %) as in *fig. 86***
- Bed adhesion: Brim (width: 6 mm; lines: 15; inside: no)

"Ribbon Part 1" & "Ribbon Part 2:
(Printing time: approx. 4 h) | scale larger by 1 - 2 % if it fits to tight

- Layer height: 0.16 mm
- Infill percentage: 25%
- Ironing enabled: yes
- Support structure: no
- Bed adhesion: Skirt (2 lines, 5 mm offset)

10.4.5 Positioning on the printing bed (per print job):

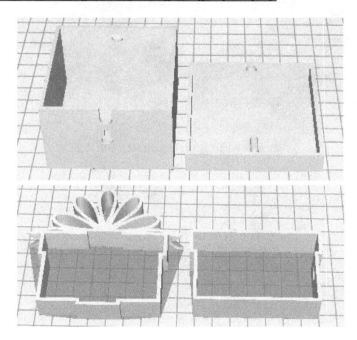

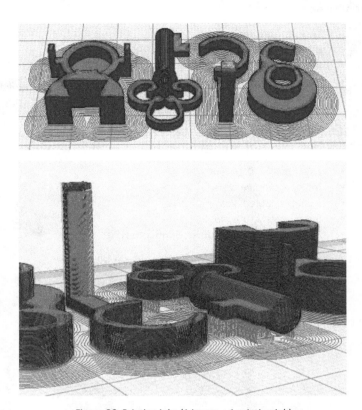

Figure 86: Printing jobs (1 image = 1 printing job)

10.5 Micro Catapult

10.5.1 Overview:

Difficulty*:
Printing time:　1.5 h
Material:　10 g

Free Download: Thingiverse
Search term: "micro catapult"
Designer: "LukeTansell"
Downloadlink: https://www.thingiverse.com/thing:1763518/files
Additionally required: ---

* (of 🏆 🏆 🏆 🏆)

10.5.2 Tips on editing and file positioning:

Positioning of all single objects as in the general view in *fig. 87:*

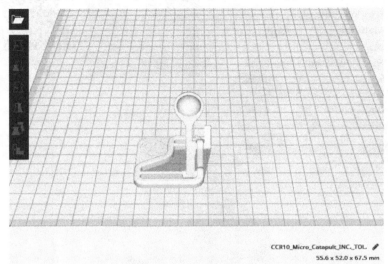

CCR10_Micro_Catapult_INC._TOL. ✎
55.6 x 52.0 x 67.5 mm

Figure 87: General view of all files to be printed (1x each)

10.5.3 Tips on slicing settings for each printing job:

"Micro Catapult INC. TOL.":
(Printing time: approx. 1.5 h)

- **Color: e.g. blue**
- Layer height: 0.2 mm
- Infill percentage: 20%
- Ironing enabled: yes
- Support structure: no
- Bed adhesion: Skirt (2 lines, 5 mm offset)

10.6 Keyring: Heart

10.6.1 Overview:

Difficulty*:
Printing time: 1.5 h
Material: 8 g

Free Download: Thingiverse
Search term: "heart key ring"
Designer: "Candice_Coreen"
Downloadlink: https://www.thingiverse.com/thing:2782690
Additionally required: ---

* (of 🖨 🖨 🖨 🖨)

10.6.2 Tips on editing and file positioning:

Rotation of all single objects as in the general view in *fig. 88:*

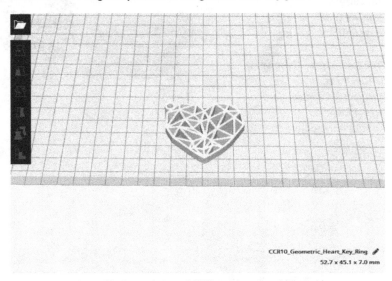

CCR10_Geometric_Heart_Key_Ring
52.7 x 45.1 x 7.0 mm

Figure 88: General view of all files to be printed (1x each)

10.6.3 Tips on slicing settings for each printing job:

"Geometric Heart Key Ring":
(Printing time: approx. 1.5 h)

- **Color: e.g. red**
- Layer height: 0.12 mm
- Infill percentage: 100%
- Ironing enabled: yes
- Support structure: no
- Bed adhesion: Skirt (2 lines, 5 mm offset)

10.7 Bearing (printed fully functionable)

10.7.1 Overview:

Difficulty*:	+
Printing time:	2.5 h
Material:	28 g

Free Download: Thingiverse
Search term: "ball bearing"
Designer: "barspin"
Downloadlink: *https://www.thingiverse.com/thing:143467/files*
Additionally required: ---

* (of 🏆 🏆 🏆 🏆)

10.7.2 Tips on editing and file positioning:

Rotation of all single objects as in the general view in *fig. 89:*

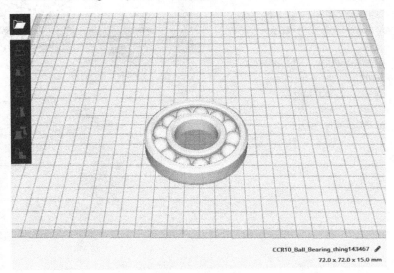

CCR10_Ball_Bearing_thing143467
72.0 x 72.0 x 15.0 mm

Figure 89: General view of all files to be printed (1x each)

10.7.3 Tips on slicing settings for each printing job:

"Ball Bearing.A.3":
(Printing time: approx. 2.5 h)

- **Color: e.g. green**
- Layer height: 0.16 mm
- Infill percentage: 20%
- Ironing enabled: yes
- Support structure: no
- Bed adhesion: Skirt (2 lines, 5 mm offset)

11 Closing Remarks

That´s it. Now it´s your turn! Start 3D printing and realize many of those fascinating projects.

If you´ve benefited from this book, you are welcome to recommend it to your friends and become a part of the growing 3D printing community. Also consider writing a short review on this book.

In the appendix you will additionally find all general slicing settings being used in this context (slicing software: Cura, 3D printer: CR-10). The settings have been specially adjusted to the first series of the "CR-10" 3D printer.

If you would like to realize your own ideas and learn how to design objects, take a look at the corresponding book: "CAD 101 – The Ultimate Beginners Guide". Also available at amazon.com.

Appendix: Slicing Settings (Cura & CR-10)

Downloadable at www.3ddruckworkshop.de/startpaket for free!

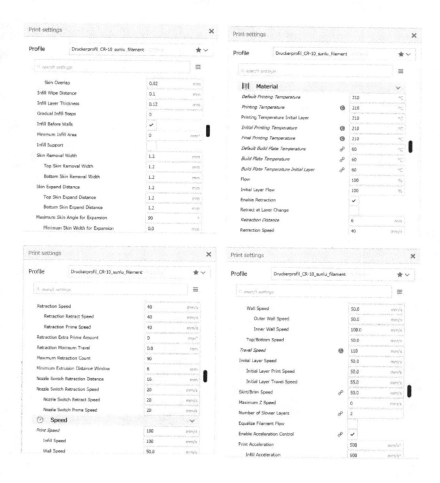

CPSIA information can be obtained
at www.ICGtesting.com
Printed in the USA
LVHW080955130422
716105LV00018B/233